GOD,

COSMOS,
AND MAN

The Role of Mind
in a Purposeful Universe

by Wayne Fields

Published by
TRIUMPHANT BOOKS
An imprint of
OUGHTEN HOUSE PUBLICATIONS
LIVERMORE, CALIFORNIA

God, Cosmos, and Man: The Role of Mind in a Purposeful Universe
by
Wayne Fields

Published in 1998

Published by
Triumphant Books
an imprint of
OUGHTEN HOUSE PUBLICATIONS
PO Box 2008
LIVERMORE, CA 94551
PHONE: (510) 447-2332
FAX: (510) 447-2376
E-MAIL: oughten@oughtenhouse.com
INTERNET: www.oughtenhouse.com

Cover design: Eric Akeson, Akeson Design
Cover photo: Images © 1997 Photodisc, Inc.

Library of Congress Cataloging in Publication

Fields, R. Wayne, 1941 -
    God, cosmos, and man : the role of mind in a purposeful universe / by R. Wayne Fields.
            p. cm.
    Includes bibliographical references and index.
    ISBN 1-880666-69-3
    1. Religion and science. 2. Consciousness. 3. Cosmology.
    I. Title
    BL240.2.F47   1997
    191--DC21

                                                                97-24588
                                                                CIP
            ISBN 1-880666-69-3

                Printed in the USA

Table of Contents

PART II: Mind and Consciousness

PART III: God, Purpose and Existence

Dedication

To my loving wife, Lorraine

Acknowledgments

I would like to thank the consumate professionals of Oughten House Publications, especially Tony Stubbs, Editor-in-Chief, and Anita Gerard, Director of Marketing. Their extensive knowledge and insights helped immensely in converting broad, technical thought into an accessible, coordinated, properly marketed whole. These sterling individuals are not responsible for any remaining errors or miscues of composition, interpretation, or clarity. I am the ultimate culprit.

Preface

In my young life, I was raised in a protestant, church-going environment. The setting was cordial, at least to the extent I can now recall, and no particularly unpleasant experiences come to mind. Nevertheless, from about the age of nine or ten, I began to question some religious dogma and think about human existence. In parallel, and presumably independently, a deep-seated internal belief in solid fact developed. As my teen years approached and appeared, I began to wonder if we could not circumvent religion's blind faith and achieve direct knowledge of our existence.

I stayed in school continuously, throughout graduate studies after completing college, and finally achieved my dream of becoming a practicing scientist. The immediate work was not concerned with lofty topics like life and existence, but I continued to read and think about such subjects as an area of strong personal interest. Eventually, through professional endeavors, I came to do a lot of business and scientific writing. Finally, about fifteen years ago, the thought of writing about my recreational passion came to mind. Sometimes it is much easier to think than to do, but, eventually, I finally decided to muster the discipline to commit thought to paper.

The universe has always struck me as a fascinating place. Not only is the fabric of the world strewn with incredible structure and activity, but to me there is something terribly exciting about the mystery of how everything works — and why? That is the real question, why? Why are we here? And given that we do exist, why in the world do we need the universe? If everything is about us, if we are the center of attention, then why not just have the earth, period? What on earth is the reason for the mind-bending diversity of contents and vast expanse of the universe?

We live in an astonishing age. Only in this century, and really only in the last couple of decades, has known fact risen to provide a realistic study of existence. It hasn't yet been thirty years that we have known that the universe had a specific beginning (about 15 billion years ago in the 'big bang' event), and only early in this century did we establish the existence of other galaxies distinct from our own Milky Way. We also have only recently obtained a reasonable idea about the nature of mind and consciousness.

We must take care not to be too smug. Our knowledge is large, solid and growing rapidly. nevertheless, there is much that we don't as yet know. The ultimate goal is to acquire sufficient detailed understanding about the universe that we can explain, in principle, what makes up all matter and how every kind of interaction occurs. Throughout history, our model of the laws of nature has changed many times. However, this century, major breakthroughs have occurred, and the details of our understanding seems to be converging on ultimate truth. In addition, there is a reasonably strong consensus that we are on the brink of another revolutionary step in understanding of nature and, hopefully, in turn, ourselves.

The present book is about the intersection of consciousness and the universe, about the purported role of consciousness in the workings of the universe at the highest level. To me, it is inconceivable that the stupendous action and organization apparent in the universe, occuring as far as we can see in every direction, is not somehow related to the presence of intelligence. Without knowledgable observers, what's the point of it all? The major theme of this book is that widespread intelligence, most likely distributed throughout the universe, probably contributes fundamentally, now or in the future, to organization and function.

The present treatise is a synthesis, not an exhaustive analysis focused on one facet of knowledge. The level of discourse is accessible to the general reader, especially those with at least some science or experience in the popular science literature. No mathematics have been employed. Also, an attempt has been made to avoid complicated terminology or jargon. However, my feeling is that some level of adherence to technical accuracy is paramount. When discussing various fields, it is crucial to employ precise terminology so that material contained here can be integrated with independent writings.

Discussion draws on diverse areas in the biological (wet) and physical (dry) sciences. The inherent breadth of discussion precludes intricate background material in all areas. Nevertheless, certain key subjects are carefully developed through orchestrated description and example. Also, a broad spectrum of other literature, much accessible to the general reader, is presented under 'Suggested Reading' at the end of the book.

Man's role in the universe cannot be adequately discussed without the treatment of religious issues. A main theme is that science has come to address many religious issues better than religion. Nevertheless, this book is not about religion, but rather a discourse about modern understanding regarding issues that were formally addressed only religiously.

My motive for writing this book was a conviction that we really matter, and that we can gain ultimate access to at least most information about existence. However, but that the average person's world view has not caught up with the remarkable knowledge that is at hand or seems imminent. This book is intended to help bridge the lay/professional information gap, and to stimulate new ideas about human and cosmic existence.

Chapter 1
Existence and Our Place in the Universe

Matter and Mind

Are we significant or not? That is, do humans have a role in the universe? This book supports an emphatic YES!

So what is it about the humble human state on our tiny planet that could possibly impact, now or in the future, the vast universe at large? It would seem that any such influence must somehow relate to our intelligence, in other words, the human mind. That is the story of this book, a view of human brain function, and of consciousness and intelligence in general, and how mind may be integrated into the very fabric of our evolving universe.

Our attention will be centered on two entities, matter and mind. Most basically, as we will see, the known universe is a gargantuan system of partially organized matter. We will also find that the material counterpart of the mind, the brain, is made up solely of the same stuff as everything else. Thus mind comes from just another form of matter, quite highly organized for sure, but simply matter just the same.

The Dynamic Universe

To lay some background, a look around the universe shows it to be everywhere teeming with fabulous displays of organization and energy. At all levels, from subatomic to cosmic, countless examples of majestic order, beauty and seemingly purposeful activity are manifest.

Man has been in awe of nature and the heavens since the dawn of modern humans tens of thousands of years ago. Yet we are all born and live without a manual or other guide to describe how the world works. As a result, throughout life, each of us must ultimately confront alone the questions of meaning and purpose. Religions aside, for most people, such concerns remain largely buried under the incessant onslaught of daily activities. However, from time to time, many come to objectively reflect on the ultimate questions of existence, our place in the universe, and the nature of the universe itself.

To modern science, the universe appears to be made up of a large number of hierarchical layers of organization. The observed layers are entwined through remarkable interrelationships, the laws of nature, cryptically hidden from easy access but revealed by diligent and skillful probing. And as studies advance, we continue to define more and more detail but also, in turn, additional support for a startling elegance and simplicity of underlying truth.

For instance, latest theory depicts the searing fireball of the big bang (the origin of the universe, as revealed by modern science) as composed of an enormous collection of a very few basic subatomic particle types, all interacting through one unique universal force. The latter world, although extremely massive, was fundamentally a very simple system. Alternatively, today's universe is governed by four forces (gravity; electromagnetism; the strong nuclear force; the weak nuclear force). Each of the four forces of the modern era appear on the surface to be independent. However, physicists now believe that today's forces are really special embodiments of the same unique universal force that governed all matter and its interactions during the big bang.

Momentous implications arise from our current knowledge of the history of the universe and the laws of nature. The universe began as a very simple system, and has since evolved such that some of the matter has become progressively more organized. Extended structure has appeared at every level of scale, from the atomic to the cosmic. At the atomic level, atoms appeared very early, but have evolved in type and in complexity as the universe advanced. On the large scale, galaxies arose later than atoms, and there are now organized systems of galaxies and even systems of galactic systems (an even higher level of order on a much grander scale of distances). At some point, life appeared, apparently adding a means to evolve far higher levels of complexity, ultimately including intelligence.

Importantly, not only has the present universe achieved the partial organization of matter, but it seems quite capable of evolving further. Also, the organization is not at all random, when taken in broad perspective. By this is meant that the organization seen at various scales, from the very small to the very large, is functionally integrated to a remarkable degree. The four forces of nature that we now experience work harmoniously in all realms, from the subatomic and atomic, through the middle dimensions that we experience directly (our bodies; objects around us), and at dimensions comparable to the solar system, our Milky Way galaxy, galactic clusters and superclusters, and the entire universe itself. The natural laws appear ideally suited to effect and perpetuate cosmic evolution and the continued development of 'interesting' (functionally meaningful) examples of higher and higher complexity.

Is it possible for such an incredibly diverse yet meticulously integrated universe to exist without purpose? I think not. In the face of overwhelming structure, and given that the universe continues to evolve in seemingly brilliant and inspiring ways, it is hard to avoid the view that we must be momentary spectators to the unfolding of some grand purposeful process.

Goals of the Present Book

So the goals of the present book can now be stated more clearly, formulated as the following six Central Questions:

1. *How Does Matter Come to Create Organized Structure?* Recently discovered, broad-based properties of matter will be examined that reveal a striking propensity for the spontaneous progressive evolution of material complexity;

2. *What is the Nature and Makeup of Mind?* We will examine the brain and mind in general, and its supreme earth-bound form, human consciousness, to see how mind really relates to the matter from which it is made;

3. *What is the Nature and Makeup of the Universe?* The universe is composed solely of matter and forces. To later put mind in a proper cosmic perspective, it is important to understand some basics of matter and its interactions;

4. *What is the Role of Mind in the Universe?* As will be shown, matter spontaneously organizes, organizes further, and then continues to organize, seemingly without end. So far, from our earthbound perspective, mind is the highest organized state that has been observed;

5. *What is the Meaning and Significance of Humanity?* Our existence and significance has been a paramount target of inquiry and speculation since the dawn of human consciousness. We will argue that humanity has a definite role in the grand scheme of universe evolution; and

6. *What Can we Say about Universal Purpose and God?* In the process of developing the other cited issues, some intriguing ideas logically appear concerning the purpose of the universe and the nature of god.

We will refer to and develop detailed data and ideas about these six Central Questions at various points in the book. Also, each question will be specifically answered, to the best of current knowledge, in the final chapter.

These are really the ultimate questions of all time. The objective here is to see what current scientific knowledge can tell us about matter, existence, and purpose, and further to embellish known fact with cautious speculation. This effort is thus an interpretation of what advancing science can reveal today about issues previously restricted by the lack of formal knowledge to the religious realm.

Following the current introductory chapter, this book is organized into three Parts:

- *Part I (Chapters 2-4)* develops the concept that matter has the inherent propensity to self-organize. This idea of self-organizing matter is absolutely critical to the entire message of the book. The reason is that all other facts, conclusions and speculations creating the central threads of the present treatment directly depend on matter's spontaneous tendency to self-organize. Such tendencies have only recently been recognized as a major, broad based attribute of matter in general. From earth, the ultimate expression of self-organizing matter is life, and more specifically, the development of higher intelligence. Part I primarily addresses Central Question [1].

- *Part II (Chapters 5-7)* provides a deep analysis of consciousness and of the unique advanced form termed self-consciousness found in humans. In addition, Part II examines the interface between matter and mind, the classic mind-body problem, subjecting this historically elusive topic to modern scrutiny and interpretation. The main conclusions drawn from Part II show that the mind is solely the result of brain function which, in turn, is purely made up of ordinary matter. However, this is matter in its highest and best use, the human brain being the most complex system in the known universe. Part II primarily addresses Central Question [2].

- *Part III (Chapters 8-10)* further develops concepts about mind and matter, and then ties together all topic threads from Parts I and II to address the remaining four goals, Central Questions [3] through [6]. Even though current scientific information is incomplete, we will see that credible ideas can at last be created and debated regarding the ultimate questions about ourselves and our universe. Key conclusions include the likelihood that consciousness (mind) plays a prominent role in our naturally evolving universe, an enormous system that is found to be purposeful but not directed toward a preordained end point. Also, we will see that god may come to be understood in forms quite distinct from common belief.

To plausibly build the whole story, a number of major background topics are felt essential to set the stage for advancing discussion. The rest of this chapter is devoted to an initial pass at some of the crucial groundwork. The first topic relates to the idea of systems of belief, human constructs to which we, both as individuals and as groups, are tightly bound.

Systems of Beliefs

We as individuals typically have a large assortment of beliefs. Beliefs vary according to source (e.g., education; experience; indoctrination) and method of receipt (e.g., logic; transference; blind-faith). The structure of the particular society in which the reader lives is in essence a construct of a multitude of belief systems, controlling the family structure, courtship and marriage, money and property ownership, laws and their means of enforcement, and a host of others. Many beliefs are wrong, by virtue of incoherence, conflicts with other beliefs, or due to contradictions with known (technically established) facts.

Man incessantly seeks answers to the profound questions of existence and universal purpose. Yet we seem to lack the discipline to wait for the truth. Humans throughout history have tended to retreat into various unfounded belief structures when faced with that which could not be directly and immediately explained. The most ubiquitous class of belief systems are collectively termed religion, but there are countless other situations where we see a similar approach of substituting artificial contrivance for known fact.

From a practical standpoint, we tend to avoid the unknown in navigating daily life, selecting mates, road or walking routes, election candidates, investments, food and an unending list of other items based on past familiarity and the comfort of identity. Favoring the known often serves us well in avoiding trouble. However, in the process, we may miss exposure to superior alternatives.

It is important to counterbalance the tendency to seek comfort in unchallenged belief by attending to logical and rational methods of study and introspection. Of course, the foremost system of thought dedicated to the careful and methodical study of ourselves and of nature is science. In addition, notwithstanding the many remaining unsolved mysteries, to date, science has worked very well. This in itself reveals a remarkable feature of the universe, the fact that evolved beings have achieved the ability to study and interpret human existence and the mechanisms of the cosmos.

As stated previously, the present book takes a broad look at what science can now say about the universe and our place therein. Many with strong religious beliefs reject such a notion as demeaning to faith and to god. But any person or religion unwilling to examine what science has to say about our world and our presence seems arrogant and unwise. It is incredibly naive to suppose that the superior organizing mechanism of the universe, whatever that might be, would choose to ignore fact and/or honor us for doing so.

Science and the Question of Existence

Modern man of at least the Western persuasion has in general attributed cosmic planning and its execution to god. Since primordial humans arose from primate ancestors, virtually every primitive group or emerging society has turned to collective spirits or a single deity to explain the unknown.

About four hundred years ago, science began to conflict with religion by challenging the view of a sheltered place for humans within a universe designed and manipulated by god. Early on, the scientific onslaught seemed to reduce human importance and stature in the universe. Humankind and the earth were no longer the center of the world, but were reduced to a bystander role in an immense, indifferent cosmic machine. This early legacy made the average person leery and suspicious of the upstart discipline of science, which was depicted as threatening and debasing.

Contemporary opinion polls show that, even today, the normal populace (statistically, of course; there are many exceptions) show a very poor understanding of even local influences of nature. A general understanding of science is far more remote yet. For a majority of the masses, religion rather than science has by far the deepest and most enduring influence on the internal world view and the conduct of daily life.

Of course, science does effect our lives, but technically, not intellectually. Through pervasive success, science has quietly come to dominate the way most of us exist. The reason is that science has been by far the most consistent means discovered to predict the future. Humankind has learned how to control many facets of the environment for sustenance and pleasure, and has further mastered a tremendous amount of information about places, things and influences throughout the universe. The enormous extent of our information, coupled with the fact that most key facts have been repeatedly confirmed through independently replicated observations or using distinct approaches, tells us something very deep about the regularity of the universe. We have come to label the observed universal consistencies as the laws of nature.

The lack of even a cursory scientific sense by most earthly citizens, even in the supposedly enlightened Western world, is a serious indictment of contemporary educational processes. Even the unfinished science of today has profound implications relative to the place of humans in the universe and therefore to our very understanding of self.

The unbelievable beauty and incredible sense of purposefulness experienced through even a limited understanding of science as it relates to human existence should not be reserved for the select scientific community. The argument here is not for a world of quantum mathematicians, but rather for informal perspective. Although absolute answers are not yet available, each of us should have the right and take the opportunity to review and contemplate at least a modest sense of present knowledge. Then, each person would be in a position to develop a solid view of being and its relation to the universe, based on a personal selection of beliefs to fill the ever-shrinking gaps in known fact.

Science arose in spite of medieval indifference and even contempt. Since then, science has revealed startling insight and understanding regarding many topics previously restricted to the blind obedience of religious belief. In contrast to depicting humans as incidental players thrust on a stage of impersonal physical forces, we will come to explore a view that conscious beings (mind) may be a fundamental feature of the universe tied perhaps to its very purpose. The incredibly beautiful universe that emerges from such a hypothesis seems to portend far more meaning and beauty for humankind and for each individual than a world of dictated design and frequent almighty intervention. At one extreme, specifically, the new view advocated here, is the notion of a self-organizing universe that purposefully evolves to produce ever more sophisticated organization and meaning. To most who have compared, the latter system is far more satisfying and meaningful than a world based on blind obedience and where physical laws are subject to regular manipulation by management (god).

This book addresses the most profound questions of human existence and purpose. As mentioned, the adopted vantage point is that of the mind and its role in the cosmos. Key topics include life, consciousness, our place in the universe, and what the universe is all about. Of course, complete answers are not available. Here, the goal is to offer a selective scientific summary and interpretation of humankind's still limited but rapidly growing knowledge about existence and the cosmos.

We live in a remarkable age amidst an explosion of data about ourselves and our place in the universe. The earth has existed for nearly five billion years. Modern humans arose some tens of thousands of years ago. The age of true science just began about 400 years ago, and the existence of other galaxies has been known only since the 1920s. You and I have the unabridged privilege to exist during the first few decades when any realistic objective assessment of physical existence has been possible. By way of a different perspective, the last 50 years collectively represent only one hundred millionth (1:100,000,000) of earth's history and on the order of one-thousandth (1:1,000) of the history of modern man.

There are some learned individuals that question whether we can ever approach an understanding of existence. However, many scientists are now vigorously pursuing what is termed the Theory Of Everything, a penultimate theory of matter and its interactions, and believe that such a construct is both

possible and feasible. I personally believe not only that we can and will discover the Theory of Everything, but that this achievement will provide significant insight to existence. This book collects and interprets key facts from the
physical and biological sciences, consistent with the present intermediate state
of \, on the breathtaking path to deeper cosmic insight.

Fundamental Assumptions

Before embarking on more detailed topics, it is essential to specify critical
definitions and mention several prime assumptions that underlie the current
work. Unfortunately, a number of terms central to later discussion have been
loosely employed in the popular literature — a situation that can lead to confu-
sion and misinterpretation:

Universe. The universe will be operationally defined to encompass all
material and influences that (apparently) arose in the big bang and that are
'observable' to us (detectable by whatever means); for completeness, note that
some versions of modern cosmology portray our big bang as having been merely
one of many occurring in a larger super-universe; where the context is believed
clear, the term cosmos or world will be used interchangeably with universe;

Life. Life is very difficult to define. Whatever we list as criteria for life
can also be found in material that we would say is non-living. In line with the
subject matter of the present treatise, a living organism will be characterized as
a highly complex and organized system that not only reproduces but also conveys a detailed plan for duplicating the same reproductive process to future
progeny (many additional criteria will be developed in Chapter 4);

Mind. We adopt the broad view that to say something is a mind is to say it
has the capacity to think. In more restrictive terms applicable to humans, mind
is the thing that: a) senses and perceives external events; b) internally feels,
remembers, recalls, and imagines, based on internal stores and external happenings; c) monitors and manages, through attention mechanisms, 'interesting' (not-subconscious) eventualities; and d) wills and instigates influences on
the outside world;

Consciousness. Consciousness will be used here to denote the state of
ongoing awareness, thought, emotion and volition that is directly experienced
and that is characteristic of advanced, independent control. Consciousness is
not a unique constellation of attributes or processes, because different levels or
types of consciousness are possible (for example, in humans, we identify many
states of consciousness, including sleep, dreaming, relaxation, the fully awake
state, heightened arousal, inebriation, etc.); and

Self-Consciousness. This is meant to represent an advanced level of consciousness, limited (on earth) basically to humans, where the conscious system is aware of being aware (is conscious of being conscious). Perhaps a key here is a deep model of self, for use in self-reference. In fact, one hypothesis is that self-consciousness in the human is due to the dynamic, ongoing comparison of abstractions of present and past experience with a permanently maintained and updated frame of reference based on a complex body-image.

Much more will be said about each of the above terms throughout the present book. For many of us, there is a compelling tendency to relate mind, consciousness and self-consciousness with life and, in particular, humans. However, a rigid tie to humans, earth life, or the organic chemistry of life on earth would be counter to current intention. Here, in general, even organic life shall not be considered a requirement for the display of intelligence.

Integrating Physical Law and the Life Sciences

This book draws upon two large (artificially separated) disciplines, the physical and the life sciences. First, the laws of nature (physical science) will be used to provide a backdrop on the rules any ultimate Theory of Everything must meet. Basically, despite its name, the Theory of Everything is directly focused only on the physical sciences as applied to non-living material. Then, contemporary knowledge in the life sciences will be employed to show how matter that is alive, particularly the human variety, relates to the vastly much larger domain of non-living matter.

It is important to realize that the distinction between the living and non-living realms is somewhat arbitrary. More will be said about such a distinction later. For now, suffice it to say that: a) all living matter is made of the same atoms and molecules as non-living substance; and b) careful examination reveals that the line between the living and non-living is definitely blurred.

At our present level of understanding, the laws of nature are expressed in many different ways. Some are revered as cornerstones of our whole world view (e.g., that energy cannot be created or destroyed), while others are considered provisional until we can discover the deepest truth or at least better midpoint renditions (e.g., perhaps surprising to some, Quantum Theory and also Relativity Theory). An all-encompassing theory that explains everything does not yet exist, but we do possess theories concerned with identifiable realms that have stupendous power. Both Quantum Theory and Relativity Theory are striking examples. Certainly these modern theories represent baseline truth in some restricted fashion and to some limited degree.

The latter point needs emphasis. Knowledge advances with countless small refinements of detail, punctuated by occasional dramatic changes in major theories or systems of thought. But supplanted theories may continue to have considerable utility, still representing various situations very well under the right circumstances. It is just that the new theories are typically more general, being applicable to an even broader set of conditions. For instance, the Theory of Relativity replaces large domains of classical physics in principle. However, for most terrestrial and celestial endeavors, classical physics still works very well and is much easier to use. The complex methods of Relativity Theory are only invoked when no other approach will do.

The edifice of the scientific method is predictability. Any theory or law of nature must be predictive to endure. Discrepancies fashion the advance of knowledge, pointing out weaknesses in existing theories and providing specific criteria that refined theories must meet. The driving force of theory evolution is conformity with rigorous, documented observation. Success in one situation does not assure that a theory is correct, because departures from the model may arise in other circumstances. But deviations from theory are extremely enlightening, revealing without question that the construct needs improvement. The strength of a theory is measured by how well it performs in as many relevant circumstances as can be devised.

Overview of the Universe — Which Reality Is Real?

For perspective, the universe is believed to have begun 15 billion years ago in a stupendous explosion termed the big bang (on an advanced level, the exact age is undergoing active debate and further research, but such considerations are unimportant here). The big bang is viewed by most as not having happened in space and time, but rather as representing the actual creation of space and time. Thus, space and time did not even exist prior to the big bang. Current theory predicts the nature and structure of matter and of forces (interactions between elements of matter) beginning as early as an infinitesimal fraction of the first second after the big bang event. The reason that such detailed knowledge is available about such remote time intervals is that the constituents of the universe at that point were extremely simple. The world was composed of a limited, describable mix of lawful subatomic particles and electromagnetic radiation existing at enormous temperatures and pressures, and nothing else.

Einstein's Theory of Relativity teaches that there is an upper limit to how fast cause-and-effect influences can spread — the speed of light. Light travels 300,000 meters in each second (through a vacuum), completing, as an illustration, a round trip to the moon and back in just under three seconds. Astronomical distances are often expressed as a multiple of the light year, the distance that light travels through a vacuum (or the near vacuum of space) in a year.

In the latter vein, earth is surrounded by a boundary in all directions with a radius of 15 billion light years, the maximum distance of causal interaction moving at the speed of light since the big bang. The confines of the latter boundary we shall term the observable universe (as mentioned previously, by observable, we really mean using any mode of detection, not just visual sightings). The actual universe may be larger, and in fact is believed by many to be infinite. Note that, as time passes, the observable universe grows in diameter, and so new material is continually entering the system. Henceforth, references to the observable universe will be shortened to just "universe."

As the primordial soup created by the big bang explosion has coasted outward with time, events ensued that led from the initial simplicity of particles and radiation to the complexity evident today. An instructive analogy is that the four forces that are evident today (gravity; electromagnetism; the strong nuclear force; the weak nuclear force) successively 'froze out' of the universe as it cooled due to expansion. This led to a succession of distinct cosmic epochs characterized by differing environments (distinct mixes and make-ups of matter and radiation) during the first seconds, minutes and beyond. As a prominent example, after about 100,000 years, matter and electromagnetic radiation 'decoupled' and have since evolved relatively independently. As the evolution of the universe continued, large-scale clumps of matter interacted predominantly through gravitation to create the distributed systems of star-studded galaxies and other material that we see today. In contrast, most electromagnetic radiation has traveled free of important influences with matter, and now represents what is termed the cosmic microwave background (one of the cornerstones of evidence supporting the big bang theory).

The components of the universe, believed to be entirely composed of matter (ultimately made up of subatomic [quantum] particles) and forces (technically, embodied in quantum entities called force quanta), have been found to follow predictable rules of engagement. We term such regularities the laws of nature. But what is the origin of the laws?

From one perspective, there are two possibilities. First, there may really be laws of nature that are constant or at least that change predictably. On the other hand, it could be that there are no laws at all, and that the dependability we see may be illusory. The evidence to date strongly argues for regular laws that also do not change with time.

As an illustration, we can study a substantial amount of physics elsewhere in the universe through observations of visual and other forms of electromagnetic radiation (gamma rays, x-rays, ultraviolet rays, infrared rays, microwaves, radio waves, etc.) and, much closer to home, matter (subatomic particles, originally misnamed as cosmic rays). It is found that the observed physics is the same everywhere we have looked. This is all the more compelling since, as we look farther and farther from earth, we are essentially looking back in time (for instance, the light reaching here from sources 10 billion light years away was emitted when the universe was only one-third its present age of 15 billion years).

So, accepting that the universe has fixed laws of nature, are the laws immutable or subject to change? Are the laws the only influence on what we see, or are supernatural interventions possible? Perhaps someone or something such as god set the laws and, from time to time, continues to pull a few strings. Or, at the other extreme, maybe the universe is rigorously structured with fixed laws, but has the propensity to evolve automatically. Finally, some combination of controlled and self-evolving systems may be manifest. This book strongly argues for a world that is governed by fixed, immutable laws and that depends for advancement (the progressive development of complexity) on pervasive, continuous, spontaneous, unplanned evolution.

The Journey Ahead

As mentioned, the ultimate goal of the present book is to review issues relevant to the purpose of the universe and also the roles of man and mind in the workings of the cosmos. A previous section of this chapter outlined six 'Central Questions' that are to be addressed.

The ultimate questions of existence, our place in the universe, and the nature of the universe itself are truly exciting topics. But developing the relevant ideas spans many diverse fields of knowledge, and broad background discussion in many disciplines is essential. For this reason, significant portions of the present book, especially Chapters 2-4 that constitute Part I, develop basic concepts deemed critical to the ultimate arguments. The emphasis of Part I on background material means that only one of the six 'Central Questions' to be addressed in the book in fact are treated to any depth. Part II advances significantly beyond groundwork presentation, and yet still is focused on only the second of the six Central Questions. Intense attention to the 'Central Questions' must await the discourse of Part III, since only at that point are the full array of properly introduced disciplines available for interpretive integration.

One of the striking views a broad study of physics and the life sciences reveals is the propensity for prodigious complexity that resides within many simple systems. Our sojourn next turns to Part I, a peek at the fascinating properties that emerge when simple systems are really allowed to show their stuff.

PART I

Self-Organization of Matter

PART I
Self-Organization of Matter

The universe began through what has come to be called the big bang event, in a state of high disorder. But now, as we look outward to the heavens and inward to atoms and subatomic phenomena, we see myriad signs of order virtually everywhere we look. The order is not complete, but is rather a partial order. Not all matter is ordered, just some, but this is quite remarkable anyway. How can it be that tremendous disorder evolved into measured order?

Research in many fields over the last few decades has led to a gradual realization by many scientists that matter has a powerful capacity to self-organize. The advent of the big bang theory on the one hand, and the discovery of self-organization on the other, has acted to solidify the viewpoint. The big bang theory told us in no uncertain terms that the universe had a fierce beginning when the highly compressed material of the cosmos was in a very simple, unordered state. Thus, organization has increased with time, at least with respect to the spectacular pockets of order we see at all scales of dimension, whether scattered through the universe as revealed by telescopes, experienced directly with our senses, or viewed through microscopes or submicroscopic probes. More recently, the recognition and study of what will be formally labeled as self-organization has shown us that matter in general, all kinds of matter and in a stupendous number of ways, automatically forms enhanced material complexity on all meaningful scales of size. Self-organization has progressively come to be seen as a general attribute of interacting matter, not a curiosity limited to a few exceptional examples.

The implications are profound. A universe composed of self-organizing material might create all sorts of structure on its own, free from outside influence or control. And if self-organizing power is strong enough, layer upon layer of complexity could eventually appear, just like simple counting and accounting by our ancestors led to the very complex (but still incomplete) understanding of mathematics today.

Part I focuses on "Emerging Properties" of matter (Chapter 2) and an elite subset thereof, "Self-Organization" (Chapter 3). These two topics are linchpins at the very heart of this book's message. And then, to conclude Part I, Chapter 4 features an in-depth look at life, by far the highest expression of self-organization known to earth beings. Importantly, Part I sets an essential stage for later scrutiny of mind and consciousness (Part II) and of our conclusions about god, the universe, and existence (Part III).

Chapter 2
Telltale Clues of Remarkable Order

The Startling Birth of New Properties

Nature is bursting with evidence of profound order all around. Look virtually anywhere and the discerning observer will discover startling order and organization. Of course, living material is the epitome of functional arrangement. But even in virtually any form of inanimate material on earth, from a speck of dust to a cloud wisp, incredible arrangement is apparent to the trained eye. The same is true of all extraterrestrial substance, at least to the extent we can study such material from afar. There is no corner of the universe that does not present telltale clues of remarkable order.

But what is the origin of this extraordinary structure and regularity? Was the universe always there, was it designed and assembled, or did the world somehow build itself? A study of the nature of the cosmos has been a serious fascination of humankind for several centuries, and is a main theme throughout this book. It will become apparent that the vast preponderance of hard evidence favors a self-evolving universe that had a definite time of origin and that has been unguided by divine tinkering. But all of the information is not yet at hand, and the subject matter is highly charged emotionally. And so, at present, each person is left on his or her own to create a personal construct of how to view the world.

Critical to an informed judgment about any subject, emotional or not, is a careful assessment of relevant data. In the latter spirit, both the present and next chapters address the subjects of emerging properties and of self-organization, respectively. The latter terms really mean roughly the same thing. Both labels refer to a natural process where component parts come together automatically to produce a more complex entity. In interesting situations, which it turns out are common, many composite entities formed from component modules are found to display new properties that just do not exist in the subunits; the whole turns out to be truly greater than the sum of its parts.

Emerging properties and self-organization actually represent different levels of the same apparently universal propensity for the automatic structuring of matter. But emerging properties refer to a broader landscape, where any type of higher function resulting from combinations of sub-elements applies. In contrast, the term self-organization will be reserved for phenomena where critical conditions are necessary for initial formation and outside energy must be continually supplied to sustain complex structure. Self-organization, then, represents a specialized elite subset of emerging properties.

The rest of the present chapter treats the broad topic of emerging properties in a fashion designed to accomplish two purposes. First, the subject of emerging properties itself must be addressed in some detail, to serve as crucial background material for later discussion. Second, the points to be developed here have been selected to also build other forms of insight, beyond emerging properties, that will be valuable for future discourse. This chapter treats emerging properties in the broadest sense, so that certain subjects involving some degree of the more restrictive topic of self-organization are included without distinction.

Before embarking on a systematic presentation, however, a quick example of emerging properties is perhaps in order to properly set the stage. The ubiquitous television set will be used for illustration.

A television set, physically, is a complicated electromechanical device that receives and processes input signals from commercial broadcast stations. Device output, in turn, is a controlled and directed electron beam confined inside a video tube (the video display) and also orchestrated mechanical vibrations of a speaker diaphragm (to create sound). The components and circuits respond to, produce and are best described in terms of voltages, currents, heat production, and other physical parameters. However, the ultimate result of television set function is the conveyance of information and entertainment, characterized by such things as ratings, air time, measures of program content, and the cost of commercials. What we are confronting here are different levels of description. Television shows exist on a higher plane of abstraction than electronic circuits and other TV hardware. Voltage has no descriptive meaning relative to television programs, and, in turn, audience ratings serve no useful purpose relative to defining the operations of an electronic circuit.

So, properties and rules at the level of television shows are quite different than those on the plane of television set components. For this reason, the new properties and rules that appeared as we ascended to the higher plane of abstraction represented by television productions can be viewed as emerging properties. No amount of knowledge about television set circuitry would allow prediction of the properties and rules that apply to television programs.

We said above that a television show resides at a higher plane of functional description than the electromechanical system that renders the animated screen and sound theatrics. Actually, overall, a television set is composed of many hierarchical layers. Although the specific designation of such layers is arbitrary and typically dependent upon the descriptive goal, an example of descending tiers beginning with those discussed above might include entertainment programs, electromechanical modules, individual electrical and mechanical components, sub-elements of components, molecules of components, atoms of components, and the subatomic particles that make up each component atom. Such tiers of successive functional description, a hierarchy of levels of abstraction, are ubiquitous in nature. Nature's towering hierarchical arrays of complexity and organization form another concept that will be encountered repeatedly throughout this book.

The following material further develops the concept of emerging properties, beginning with familiar examples from simple geometry. The discourse then continues through the more abstract topics of molecular and biochemical arrangements, and culminates with an analysis of a recently proposed model of cognitive structure. The latter topic is especially significant. Organization of the brain and of the mind are prime subjects of this book. A view of how the thoughtful mind may be assembled from non-thinking sub-elements is not only an amazing concept, but is fundamental to later discussion about the mind and consciousness.

Hierarchies & Emergence — Geometry

Zero Dimensional Space. To initiate the more formal introduction to emerging properties, the realm of a pure rectilinear geometry was chosen to free initial concepts from the complications of tangible matter. It should be realized that the following development is not meant to be a rigorous treatment of geometry, but purely a simple, intuitive model for discussion.

We begin by picturing a point. In fact, let's be even more precise and work with what technical scholars call a mathematical point. A mathematical point has no dimensions. The point does not have length, width, height, size, or any other extent. A mathematical point represents a position, but does not possess any other property such as physical dimensions or directions. The space associated with a mathematical point is said to have zero dimensions.

One Dimensional Space. Now, imagine two mathematical points positioned, say, one inch apart horizontally. Next, assume that the two points are connected with a straight mathematical line, such that the points define each respective line end (left and right). Again, since we are dealing with mathematical abstractions, the line has no width, height or size. But, the line does have one extent that a mathematical point does not — length. The line also has acquired two directions, because, at any location along the line, the concept of forward or backward is legitimate.

As we move from the zero-dimensional space of the point to the one-dimensional space of the line, the geometrical system acquires emerging properties, that of length, location along the line, and two directions. The line also retains the property of position, which can be specified, for example, as a function of either or both line end points. It is very important to understand what happened here. Referring back to the zero dimensional space of the mathematical point discussed above, it is not realistic to say that the point has no length, location or directions. The reality is that it makes no sense to even discuss length, location or direction relative to our point or, in general, with regard to any mathematical point. In a zero dimensional space, any talk of length, location or direction is not merely of zero utility, it is meaningless.

Two Dimensional Space. Now picture duplicating our one inch line three more times, and configuring the four resultant lines to form a square with each line forming one complete side. Our space now has two dimensions, the original horizontal dimension which we decided to call length, and a new dimension, perpendicular to length, which we shall term width. The space also has acquired two new directions associated with the width dimension, say, fore and aft.

Our square has four equal sides, and the array of lines that define the square, by definition, form a closed figure. Actually, we could have used lines of differing length, to produce figures of innumerable shapes. But all such two dimensional figures would possess a new emerging property not found in one dimensional lines, that of area. Also, as mentioned, we acquired two new directions, fore and aft. Finally, we can also speak about the shape of the figure we have rendered, depending on the number, length and curvature of the lines used to form the closed figure. In contrast, it is meaningless to speak of shape in a one dimensional space. The only true variables in a one dimensional space are location along the line and length, and therefore the curvature of the line has no meaning. So, all told, we have acquired four emerging properties in moving from a one to a two dimensional space, being, respectively, area, shape, and the fore-aft directions. We also have retained, in principle, all of the properties of the underlying zero and one dimensional spaces that now help to define positions and boundaries in our two dimensional realm.

Three Dimensional Space. Next, imagine duplicating the square six times and forming said elements into a cube (actually, the proper use of four squares would suffice). In doing so, we have added an additional dimension for a total of three. The new dimension, which we shall term height, is mutually perpendicular to both the length and width defined above. Along with the new dimension are two respective new directions (up and down).

The cube retains the property of position, which can be implemented, in one approach, by referring to the locations of the eight points defining corners of the cube (in fact, an appropriate three points would do). The cube also exhibits length and shape properties associated with the boundary lines of the solid cube figure. But again we see the emergence of new properties. First, for the cube, or, in general, for any three dimensional figure, a new property of volume has become manifest. It makes no sense at all to discuss the volume of a square, line or point. We also saw two new directions emerge, in association with the third dimension, up and down.

Hierarchies & Emergence — Molecular Systems

The development above addressed the abstract world of geometry. Clear demonstrations of emerging properties were found at several succeeding levels of complexity. Does such a pattern hold in the real world of tangible substance? Indeed it does.

In fact, it has been discovered that a prominent common thread pervading every nook and cranny of the universe is the existence of hierarchical levels of complexity. In the discussion above, four tiers of abstraction within a simple rectilinear geometry (actually, more tiers could have been discussed as well) were studied to introduce the concept of multi-plane description, unmarred by real world distractions. In an analogous way, the material to follow confronts several hierarchical systems, but from the real world. The particular systems chosen have the added benefit of also being relevant in other ways to the discussion of upcoming chapters.

To begin, one simple classification of universe contents places every entity as a form of either matter or force quanta. Force quanta are special subatomic entities that collectively convey all interactions between elements of matter. During most of the twentieth century, four distinct forces of nature have been recognized: electromagnetism, gravity, the strong nuclear force (the most prominent force in the subatomic realm), and the weak nuclear force (responsible for radioactivity and other more subtle subatomic processes not controlled by the strong nuclear force). Physicists have found that the most effective way to describe how different entities of matter interact is to say that the force between them is conveyed by an exchange of force quanta. A different form of force quanta conveys each force, so that photons transmit electrical and magnetic forces, gravitons mediate the gravitational force between gravitating bodies, and so forth. A detailed discussion of the forces of nature is beyond the present treatment, but excellent discussions can be found through the Suggested Readings section at the end of the book.

Our immediate interest centers on matter itself. All of the substance we see in the universe is made up of matter. And various forms of matter are manifest in a remarkable hierarchical array of structure and accompanying function. Here, several lower-level tiers in the structural hierarchy of matter will be briefly discussed to provide another perspective on emerging properties. It is important to realize that the following review is quite simplistic, and omits considerable detail in the interest of clear focus on the topic at hand.

We are taught in early science classes that the solid matter of our environment is composed of atoms. Atoms, in turn, are composite structures, being made up generally of a mix of protons and neutrons in the atomic nucleus, the nucleus being enshrouded with orbiting electrons. It turns out that protons and neutrons (collectively termed nucleons) are also composite structures, forming the next tier of complexity above systems of entities termed quarks.

Quarks. We begin the present story at the quark plane of complexity, which, to the best of current knowledge, is the most fundamental level of matter (neither quarks, nor electrons for that matter, can be further dissected into composite parts). Except for ordinary mass, quarks are defined primarily by characteristics not apparent in the nucleons produced when quarks join together in permitted combinations. For example, quarks experience an effect called confinement that strangely allows individual quarks a level of freedom when very close to other appropriate quarks, but never permits quarks to exist in isolation. The latter effect is related to a unique quark attribute whimsically termed color charge, a label for the subclass of the strong nuclear force that binds quarks together. In addition, Quarks exhibit properties of fractional electrical charge and a curious spin (a strange sub-nuclear form of particle angular momentum).

Nuclear Matter. Protons and neutrons are each formed by triplet combinations of quarks (three quarks bound together), and possess mass conveyed from the quark level of complexity. But new properties appear as well. Properties emerging at the level of nucleons (and other less common subatomic particles) include composite spin (the sum of the spins of the component quarks), integer electrical charge (the sum of the fractional electrical charges of the component quarks), and decay (particle lifetime). None of these properties have comparable meaning below the subject tier of complexity.

Combined in permitted ways, nucleons (protons and neutrons) unite in numerous mixtures to form the nuclei of various atoms. Nuclei exhibit additional emerging properties, beyond the constituent nucleons, such as nuclear energy levels.

Atomic Matter. A sea of protons, neutrons and electrons flying about would not resemble our common view of matter at all. But combined in a very special way, the latter particles beget atoms. And atoms are the subunits that make up all ordinary matter that we encounter in our immediate environment.

As mentioned previously, atoms generally have a mixture of protons and neutrons in the nucleus, the latter entity being enveloped in a swarm of orbiting electrons. Electrically neutral atoms have an equal number of positively charged protons (residing in the nucleus) and orbiting negatively charged electrons. Low-energy atoms range in diameter from about 1-5 Angstroms (10^8 Angstroms equals one centimeter), and the three-dimensional swarm of electron orbitals expands as an atom ascends to higher states of excitation. Free atoms are described by such attributes as atomic number (position in the Periodic Table of the Elements), atomic weight, chemical properties, a tier of sizes (dependent on the species of atom and its level of excitement), and state of ionization (a charged state of the atom, caused by one or more electrons being missing). None of the latter properties or definitions listed generically for atoms have any meaning at the previously discussed subatomic levels.

Molecular Matter. A molecule is a group of atoms bound together. The simplest molecules have only two atoms. Two atoms of oxygen bound together form a molecule of oxygen, symbolized as O_2. One atom of carbon combined with one atom of oxygen results in a molecule of CO, carbon monoxide. Molecules can range in complexity to many thousands of atoms, the higher atom counts being especially found in association with living material.

Typical attributes identified with simple molecules include molecular weight, chemical properties, rotations (rotational energy levels), and inter-atomic vibrations (vibrational energy levels involving individual pairs of atoms within the molecule). Molecular weight and chemical properties are similar to counterpart characteristics described for atoms. But again, we see the appearance of new attributes, exemplified here by rotations and vibrations. For comparison, discussing any kind of rotation or vibration in an isolated atom makes no sense; rotation and vibration arise from the relative motions of multiple atoms.

Emerging Phenomena in Gases. There are many paths of choice to discuss higher levels of material organization. For current purposes, a consideration of certain emerging phenomena has been selected that is best illustrated relative to the behavior of gases.

For simplicity, a large fixed cubical volume, say several cubic meters, of gas at room temperature will be considered. The nature of the gas is unimportant, because all gases under the stated conditions behave as if made up of rapidly moving independent, rigid spherical entities that undergo perfectly elastic collisions (two molecules retain all energy of motion after a collision; no energy is lost to the surroundings).

Let's begin with one molecule of our gas (or, alternatively, we could use a gas formed purely of atoms, such as argon or another noble element). The molecule is flying around inside the cube, rebounding from each container wall that is encountered at an appropriate angle as if it were a light beam reflecting off a mirror. But from outside the cube, which we will assume is opaque, there is no detectable effect, and so we are unaware that the molecule is there.

The behavior of the system will now be examined as additional gas molecules are added. At first, as molecule after molecule is injected into the container, there is still no effect detectable by gross measurements of normal environmental variables. But as the molecular count is progressively increased by orders and orders of magnitude, finally achieving roughly the density of air, we observe along the way the emergence of two common environmental parameters, temperature and pressure, that were not present before.

Temperature, as normally experienced, results collectively from the average velocity (actually, kinetic energy) of the gas molecules (a measurement that would have the same result anywhere in the chamber, since all chamber areas are freely communicating and are therefore in equilibrium). We are assuming the use of a physical outdoor thermometer, so that a small number of gas molecules would have too little an effect for detection (Theoretically, physicists ascribe temperature to even a single moving particle, proportional to its velocity. However, such a convention is not relevant to our viewpoint here, the world of common experience). In essence, we have witnessed the emergence of temperature as a collective property of large numbers of moving molecules.

We also find an equal pressure on all of the walls of our cubical container. Gross pressure is the sum total of the force per unit area exerted by individual molecules striking any small subject area on the container surface. The pressure should be the same at any point on the container, because the gas molecules are in equilibrium throughout the chamber. Theoretically, as with temperature, one gas molecule might be said to exert a pressure, because it does from time to time hit a given wall of the cube. However, such a description would be bizarre. Pressure is not meant to imply an irregular recurrent impulse, but rather a steady, more or less sustained action. In addition, the impulse of one molecule bouncing off a cube wall would display an incredibly minuscule strength (far below the ability of routine detection by a macroscopic pressure transducer). In contrast, our familiar pressure sense is the ongoing average result of trillions of molecules persistently bombarding the wall (at room temperature and pressure, on the order of one million million molecules would be in mechanical contact with the wall during individual bouncing events at any given instant). So here we have seen the emergence of a second property, pressure, as a collective property of large numbers of moving molecules.

As we saw, depending on how one defines pressure or temperature, it might be argued that even single atoms or molecules might be said to exhibit the phenomenon. Even so, a digression to the next lower level of complexity, that of subatomic particles, clearly excludes any meaning whatsoever regarding temperature or pressure. But, returning to the level of description represented by our subject gas, there is another property that clearly emerges only as the density of molecules rises to terrestrial orders of magnitude — the transmission of sound. Sound is purely a movement of disturbances through a medium made up of large numbers of interacting units (in our case molecules). Sound has no meaning below the level of complexity represented by atoms.

Hierarchies & Emergence — Biochemical Systems

So far, two unfolding series of emerging properties have been surveyed, one from abstract geometry and another from ordinary inanimate matter. In both series, totally new properties were seen to appear in each of several successive hierarchical layers of structure and description. But do similar types of impressive effects appear in more complicated and interesting systems? In fact, such phenomena not only appear, but, as cases in point, lie at the heart of understanding life and consciousness.

To demonstrate emerging properties in a key facet of living processes, an analysis of proteins has been chosen. Proteins are truly at the heart of life. While earth life also requires lipids, carbohydrates and nucleic acids as well (see Chapter 4), proteins form the most diverse and dynamic class of biological molecules. The importance of proteins (and the other main molecules-of-life classes) to our overall theme is that none of these molecular classes existed on earth when the planet formed about 4.5 billion years ago — every single protein molecule that exists here today is the result of the further natural evolution of material complexity on earth, once the planet formed. The especially complicated hierarchical structure of proteins provides a glimpse of the awesome complexity that matter can spontaneously achieve. Thus, a look at protein structure provides baseline perspective for later discussion about what it means to be alive.

Proteins are polymers. Polymers are based on extended chains of repeating units. Many common substances in the modern world are polymers, like polypropylene (fibers for fabrics and carpets) and polyvinyl chloride (PVC; phonograph records, rainwear, piping). But the interest here is with bio-polymers, polymeric compounds found in living systems.

Amino Acids. As stated, our interest here is with the proteins. Proteins are basically made up of linear chains of amino acids, with occasional branching.

The exact structure of amino acids is unimportant for the present discussion. Suffice it to say that amino acids are small molecules (10-30 atoms) that come in about 20 varieties important to life. Carbon, hydrogen, oxygen and nitrogen are found in all amino acids. Each amino acid is distinguished according to such properties as molecular weight, solubility, optical rotation of polarized light in solution, and the specific size, layout and chemical nature of the central hydrocarbon chain of the molecule (e.g.; polarity; acid-base status; number of directly-linked carbon atoms; special chemical groups).

Proteins. Linear or branched chains of amino acids with a molecular weight under 10,000 are usually termed peptides, while more ponderous assemblages are called proteins. There is no known upper limit to protein size, and some species possess molecular weights of many millions. Theoretically, the possible number of unique proteins is astronomical. Picture a string of beads, each bead representing one amino acid in a chain. Any one of the 20 amino acids can reside at any single point. Thus, even for just the first five positions of an amino acid chain, the number of alternatives is 20^5, or over 3 million. In nature, proteins with hundreds or thousands of amino acids are quite common.

Proteins are commonly characterized according to several parameters also used to define amino acids, including molecular weight, solubility, and polarity. As an illustration related to both solubility and polarity, the relative amounts of the 20 amino acids found in living tissue vary with the nature and function of the specific protein under consideration. Amino acids that have relatively pure hydrocarbon side chains (made up only of straight chains of carbon and hydrogen) predominate in the insoluble, fiber-like proteins such as collagen (a tissue-supporting protein). In contrast, the amino acids with polar side chains (where interactions involving electrical charge are significant) are relatively more abundant in the water-soluble proteins such as digestive tract enzymes.

The ascent from the level of amino acids to that of the proteins reveals striking emerging properties. Proteins reveal incredibly robust structural and functional roles in countless bio-molecular situations. By way of comparison, amino acids serve basically as sources of raw materials and energy, but feature no structural and very few higher functional roles at all.

Multi-dimensional Protein Structure. Some peptides and proteins carry out intended function predominantly as the result of the sequence of amino acids that make up the polymer chain. The arrangement of amino acids along the polymer chain determines the protein's unique identity, and is termed the *primary structure* of the protein. A change of even one amino acid can markedly alter the biochemical properties of the protein. As an example, a minor defect in the protein hemoglobin, the oxygen-carrying moiety in red blood cells, causes the serious disease called sickle cell anemia. Of four protein chains in the hemoglobin molecule, the one affected contains 146 amino acids. In sickle cell anemia, a wrong amino acid, valine instead of glutamic acid, appears in the sixth position — nothing else is changed. But this one substitution, an amino acid that features a hydrocarbon side chain replacing one that has an acidic functional group in the side chain, alters the solubility properties of the entire hemoglobin molecule and therefore disrupts overall function.

Proteins in living tissues are not simply long, flexible chains with random shape. Quite the contrary, the chain tends to exhibit segments or regions featuring coils, straight or curved stretches, kinks, bends and a host of other localized formations that are essential to proper protein function. The latter regional aspect of the protein architecture is called *secondary structure*. The alpha-helix configuration, a helical coiled arrangement (appearing like a coiled spring) that characterizes certain segments of many proteins, serves as a classic example of secondary structure.

Large protein molecules commonly display many distinct segments. As mentioned, some stretches may be in the alpha-helix configuration, others may be straight, curved or random, and still more may show kinks, twists or further irregularities. Such examples of secondary structure represent arrangements restricted to focal areas. In turn, the overall shape of the entire protein, determined collectively by all the bends, kinks, helical segments and every other type of local arrangement, is termed protein *tertiary structure*. On first order analysis, one might imagine that a protein in a particular place in the body with a given primary structure could form all sorts of regional (secondary structure) and gross three-dimensional (tertiary structure) arrangements. But such is not the case. Certain foldings of the protein chain lead to lower-energy (more stable) arrangements than do other patterns. For instance, a protein dissolved in water usually will fold in such a way that the non-polar (water-avoiding) hydrocarbon portions are tucked within the molecule, whereas the more polar (water-compatible) acidic and basic side chain functional groups are projected into the surrounding solution. The net result of these and other influences is to generally dictate a basic configuration or at least a small set of postures that the protein will typically assume.

Most proteins are composed of a single polypeptide chain. However, some proteins are formed from two or ore polypeptide chains (recall that the hemoglobin molecule, discussed above, has four chains). The extra variable of how these independent chains fit and fold together to determine the structure of the overall molecule is termed *quaternary structure*. Again, as with secondary and tertiary structure, quaternary structure is highly dependent upon minute details of the component polypeptide chains.

The importance of primary, secondary, tertiary and quaternary protein structure relative to emerging properties is profound. As mentioned in passing above, the complete profile of properties and functional interactions that characterize any protein are rigorously determined by the four subject tiers of architectural description.

Enzyme Function. A great many proteins have a structural purpose. Once in place, structural proteins basically mind their own business and carry out intended function. In contrast, another great class of proteins are the enzymes, reaction regulators (biological catalysts) that direct molecular traffic and control reactions.

The human body is characterized by an extremely complex array of inter-related chemical reaction systems. All reactions must occur at carefully con-trolled rates which can also vary moment by moment proportional to circumstances. Thousands of individual chemical components must be main-tained at proper concentrations.

Every one of the many thousands of chemical reactions occurring in a large biological system can be represented by an ordinary laboratory chemical reaction. What is extraordinary about biochemical systems is that so many reactions easily proceed at temperatures far below those that would be required in the laboratory. Life's secret is the use of catalysts, agents that control and hasten chemical reactions without being consumed in the process. In general, a catalyst, since it is not consumed, can remain available to work its magic over and over again for as long as the need exists. Catalysts are used all the time in the laboratory and in commerce. The particular class of biological catalysts, those moieties found in living material, are termed enzymes.

Clearly, the evolution of proteins capable of carrying out catalysis is a stun-ning illustration of yet another emerging property. An enzyme is the ultimate in exploitation of primary, secondary, tertiary and quaternary protein structure, creating a new level of complexity and organization. In simple form, an enzyme binds and holds reacting components in a special configuration that facilitates a particular reaction or that permits a specific reaction to occur that is otherwise not feasible. The most common model of enzyme function is that of a lock and key. The enzyme is configured just right and has chemical groups that bind with the reacting molecules to hold them in a special orientation so that the reaction, otherwise perhaps quite unlikely or slow, now can proceed with ease.

The very early evolution of proteins and of enzymes was essential for the development of life as we know it on earth. Thus, as detailed in Chapter 4, the extraordinary origin and explosive advancement of life on earth would have not been possible at all without the natural evolution of proteins (and the other molecules of life) in the pre-cellular (pre-life) epoch of earth's history.

So the evidence of modern science depicts a universe that spontaneously advanced to achieve progressively higher and higher levels of complexity. And given the special conditions on earth, there arose over time a collection of highly complex organic molecules. Eventually, such organic molecules inter-acted further to spontaneously create the first living systems. And, of course, since then, living systems have evolved to create a plethora of higher and less advanced life forms. The enormous gulf between the featureless sea of sub-atomic particles and forces of the big bang on one hand, and the intricate nuances of complex life forms on earth, is absolutely stupendous. And yet, we have direct evidence of an even more impressive level of emergence, as de-scribed in the next section.

Hierarchies & Emergence — Cognition

Life is one main topic of this book, but an even stronger theme relates to intelligence and consciousness. Here, the concept of emerging properties will be further reinforced with a look at building blocks of the mind. As we will develop in much greater detail in later chapters, the human mind is by far the most advanced level of material organization that we have observed to date in the universe.

Marvin Minsky recently developed a masterful and stimulating description about how intelligence can emerge from non-intelligence (*The Society of Mind*). Minsky argues that a functional mind can be assembled from a large number of little parts, each mindless by itself. Minsky's concepts arose from his central work in the origins and development of the field of artificial intelligence.

Minsky's model of cognition is hierarchical in structure. The overall mind is depicted as made up of a very large number of interrelated tiers. Each fundamental element at the lowest levels is termed an agent of the mind. Agents are data processing units dedicated to one and only one purpose. To accomplish anything but the most restricted elementary action requires combining the efforts of multiple agents. As one begins to ascend the hierarchy of Minsky's model, the outputs of higher and higher level agents begin to exhibit actions that seem to convey low levels of knowledge. Further advancement up the staircase of the mind leads to agents with more and more seemingly knowledgeable behavior. And yet the entire superstructure of any one, say, mid-level agent is simply built from an underlying hierarchical pyramid of individual subservient mindless processors.

For a moment, we will focus on a reasonably low-level agent viewed within the hierarchy of Minsky's model. Looking at the low-level agent, compared to agents at even lower levels, our subject unit accomplishes some special function (e.g., stacking children's blocks to make a tower), and therefore seems relatively knowledgeable, especially compared to functional capabilities at lower levels (for instance, merely grasping one block). Minsky designates agents that seem smart, at least in a given context, as agencies. But what looks like a well healed agency in one situation may be a lowly subordinate agent in another. Our block stacking unit is an agency relative to the even lower level agent for block grasping, but is purely a minor subordinate agent relative to a higher agency for designing and building a model house out of blocks.

At reasonably high levels, where function appears definitely knowledgeable, Minsky's agencies are quite similar to component units of the mind that Robert Ornstein (*The Evolution of Consciousness*) terms simpletons. Much will be said about Ornstein's exciting work in later chapters. But it is critical to clarify terminology at an early stage. In the present book, I will use the term *mindlets* as perhaps a more functional term to replace Ornstein's simpletons, both of which correspond to some reasonably high level agency in Minsky's terminology.

Minsky carefully albeit informally models, in general, all levels of mind function, from the most basic mindless action to the highest forms of intelligence. Relative to reasonably low tiers of complexity, Minsky uses at one point the example of a reduced level agency termed *Builder*. *Builder* takes control when we try to stack objects, as, for example, assembling a tower from an array of children's blocks. Viewed from the outside, *Builder* is quite knowledgeable, being able to take several blocks and assemble them in a stable stack. But as we look inside of *Builder* to see how the system works, we find that there is merely a pyramidal array composed of multiple levels of mindless agents. The hierarchical collection of agents is controlled by the uppermost agent in the agency, in this case *Builder* (Figure 2.1). *Builder* is thus an agent coordinator that calls on whatever subagents are required to complete the task of the instant. *Builder* does only one thing, the stacking of objects. And the actions are automatic but are contingent on context — *Builder* sequentially draws on those agents subordinate to *Builder* that are required to complete the assigned task, step by step (see Figure 2.1 for a more detailed explanation).

Builder is a fairly low level agency. The years and years of play by children is extremely significant — the process of child's play builds countless agents and agencies at all levels of the mind. As the child grows, more and more agents are added to existing tiers and also many new tiers are added to the growing mind's hierarchy. And, as maturity advances, the most basic agencies become more and more remote, buried under countless mounting layers of newer and higher skilled agents. As time passes, we basically forget how hard it was to learn the lowest level processes in the first place, even though such basic tiers come to provide a vast sea of mindless agents upon which we constantly draw (this enormous constellation of low-level agents largely makes up what is termed common sense). Everyone's hierarchy of mind is different, both in arrangement and in the actual roster of agents. Every mind is functionally quite unique, even those of identical twins.

Minsky shows us a bottom-up view of the mind, how intelligence can be conceived to occur as an organized assemblage of mindless data processors (agents). As will be shown later, Ornstein presents a top-down perspective of cognition, showing how the seemingly unified mind is really the result of a marvelous competitive interaction of a large number of mindlets (Ornstein's simpletons), vying to be the single mindlet allowed to assume control at any one time.

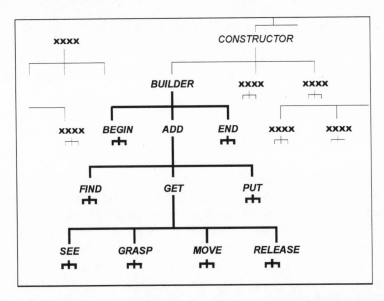

Figure 2.1 presents a schematic, adapted from Minsky* of a low-level agency termed *Builder*. *Builder* sits at the peak of a pyramidal hierarchy formed by tiers of agents, a small complement of which is shown. In the hypothetical model, three agencies occupy the highest-level plane immediately subservient to *Builder, i.e., Begin, Add,* and *End*. In turn, each of the latter three agents control a pyramidal hierarchy of subagents as well (only a few examples are shown, but, for the average intermediate-level agency, the total number of sub-levels available to a given agency could be quite large). For perspective, *Builder* is also one of several subservient agents to the next-higher tier, here labeled *Constructor*.

Builder works as follows. To start, *Builder* always activates the first (for illustration, the most leftward) agent, in this case, *Begin*. If the action has not been initiated before, *Begin* then systematically executes each agent in its most proximate hierarchical level (and, in turn, their subservient agents) until all *Begin* actions are complete. Then *Begin* passes control to *Add*. *Add* operates in the same fashion as *Begin* and all other agents, systematically calling on its subagents until all actions are completed. For illustration, three subservient agents of *Add* are shown (*Find*, *Get* and *Put*), and, further, four agents immediately subservient to *Get* are shown as well (*See*, *Grasp, Move* and *Release*).

Add works as follows. Once control has been passed to *Add* from *Begin*, *Add* activates its first subagent *Find*. *Find* then turns on, successively, agents within in its purview, descending to lower and lower sub-levels as necessary to complete all sub-tasks. Once *Find* has finished, control is passed to *Get*. In the case of *Get*, four immediate subagents have been shown in the figure. *Get* first calls on *See*, *See* executes all agencies in its highest subservient level, each of those agents descending to lower and lower levels as required to complete the action.

Control is then passed to *Grasp*, and *Grasp* carries out actions in a like manner. Once *Grasp* is done, control is passed successively to *Move*, *Release*, and then back up to *Get*. Since *Get* is now complete, control is passed to *Put*, and once *Put* is complete, control is conveyed upward to *Add*. In turn, since *Add* is now complete, control is conveyed to *End*. Finally, once *End* completes all requisite tasks in its hierarchy, control is passed up to *Builder* and the entire exercise is finished.

* Reprinted with permission of Simon & Schuster from *The Society of Mind* by Marvin Minsky. Copyright © 1985, 1986 by Marvin Minsky.

It will be restated several times throughout this book that the human brain is the most complex system that has been uncovered to date in the known universe. That such an incredibly intricate entity with truly awesome capabilities can arise from the coordinated action of huge numbers of tiny, mindless information processors is astonishing to most. But the current consensus of neurophysiologists is that the full scope of the mind is purely a result of complicated but straightforward interactions of elemental brain processes. Minsky's model provides an excellent hypothesis of how, in practice, the mind might arise from very simple structures. And such a system is an extraordinary illustration of emerging properties at their best.

The Pinnacle of Emergent Prowess

Minsky's model not only epitomizes emerging properties, but also phenomena collectively termed self-organization. The topic of self-organization is the subject of the next chapter. Recall that early in the present chapter, emerging properties and self-organization were described as displaying many similarities but also some differences. Both phenomena are similar in representing automatic processes in nature that explore and capture new levels of complexity, building on previous forms of matter to produce novel functions and capabilities. But self-organization is a narrower process forming an extraordinary high-level subset of emerging properties. Emerging properties are routinely seen to occur under very general conditions and where the input of external energy is not prerequisite to force and sustain new order. In contrast, self-organization is a specialized class of emerging properties where critical conditions are often required for unfolding and where ongoing external sources of energy are essential to maintain the unusual organized state.

The human brain certainly harbors innumerable examples of both emerging properties and self-organization. As simple illustrations, brain cell action, like all cell activity and even life itself, is a magnificent testament to energy-dependent self-organization. But the emergence of intelligent actions through the mere arrangement and selective activation of mind agents, an effect not requiring any added energy but merely the evolution of connections, is more representative of the concept of emerging properties developed above. So overall, the trillions upon trillions of small evolutionary advances that led to the human brain are certainly an inseparable mix of both general emerging properties and also of more specific self-organization.

Thus, Minsky's stirring model of the mind could have been used as an example of either emerging properties or of self-organization. The choice to present the model here was to introduce concepts about the brain and the mind early in the book. This is important because future chapters will progressively position the mind in an ever more central role in nature.

The latter idea deserves further emphasis. The best evidence to date depicts the emerging phenomenon of the human mind as the direct and sole result of past and ongoing spontaneous 'complexification' of ordinary matter. This spectacular notion carries profound implications for especially Western cultures. Many people have come to accept the existence of evolution, but somehow conceive of this powerful developmental force applying only to microbes, plants and animals, not man. But man is evolving too, and the mighty human mind is most likely a mere intermediate, local (earth bound) momentary level in matter's automatic, ever advancing complexity. These ideas are developed in much more detail as the book proceeds.

Sensational as they are, emerging properties in general take a back seat to the elegance and fabulous power of self-organization. We shall see that life, mind, consciousness and in fact the universe as a whole are majestic self-organizing systems that have come a long way but still appear to hold much more future advancement in store. And so to lay important groundwork for later discussion, it is to the subject of self-organization, the pinnacle of emergent prowess, that we now turn.

Chapter 3
The Ultimate Self-Ordering Systems

Self-Organization and the Origins of Complexity

Scientists now believe that none of the main objects and systems that make up our present physical world existed at the beginning of the universe. During and immediately following the big bang, the universe was in an essentially featureless condition, composed purely of a random mixture of the most basic primordial forces and subatomic particles. In some way, the obvious structure and complexity of the universe we now observe emerged from the simplest of states.

The fact that complex objects are found at all is amazing. Not only did the universe begin in a state of ultimate simplicity, but we now see influences everywhere that constantly tend to disrupt structure and organization. We only have to look as closely as our clothes or homes to see undeniable and often excruciating examples of deterioration and disintegration. Yet somehow, in spite of the constant onslaught of destructive influences, the universe has managed to evolve and continue to create stunning complexity. How is this possible?

Also, why is there structure and order in the universe at all? Remarkably, it is only in very recent times that, stated with the wisdom of hindsight, a sensible response has arisen. We now have a working hypothesis and some impressive albeit preliminary constructs, as discussed in more detail elsewhere, headway that will hopefully spawn even deeper understanding.

The rub here is the Second Law of Thermodynamics (the "Second Law"). This law was developed in the nineteenth century and has become a cornerstone of science. The Second Law has such bold and broad implications that it impacts virtually every action of any consequence in the universe. Thus, all of the discussion of the present chapter and much of this book must be analyzed with one eye on the implications of the Second Law.

But to initially set the stage, the basic question we must answer is as follows. The Second Law says the universe constantly runs down (moves from a more ordered to a less ordered state). So how is the accumulation of any order possible at all, anytime or anywhere?

The Second Law and Disorder

A simple chemical system will be used to illustrate and define essential concepts. Readers unfamiliar with chemistry need not shy away from the descriptions below, since the general ideas should be accessible without attention to specific detail.

We will consider a very basic chemical reaction occurring within a fixed container. Two species called reactants chemically react as the result of random molecular contact to create two different species termed products. The latter arrangement can be modeled as follows (the dual arrows imply an equilibrium state — see later discussion):

$$AB + C <===> A + BC \qquad \qquad \textit{Equation 3.1}$$

A common example of a reaction of the present form would be:

$$Metal + Salt <===> Salt + Metal \qquad \textit{Equation 3.2}$$

$$Zn + CuSO_4 <===> ZnSO_4 + Cu \qquad \textit{Equation 3.3}$$

where the example reaction involves solid zinc (Zn) and Copper (Cu) metals immersed in a water solution of the salt Copper Sulfate ($CuSO_4$) and the salt Zinc Sulfate ($ZnSO_4$).

More complex reactions may involve what are designated as intermediates, species that temporarily form as a transitional step in the reaction, a situation that can be schematically depicted as follows:

$$AB + C <===> [ABC] <===> A + BC \qquad \textit{Equation 3.4}$$

Intermediates (the [ABC] complex in the above illustration) are created and then destroyed as the reaction proceeds. The reactants and products typically spread (diffuse) equally to all parts of a confined volume of media, such as a gas or liquid solution. Thus, after time, a given chemical species has the same concentration throughout the reacting volume, although different species will typically have different concentrations. When concentrations have stabilized, we say that the reaction has reached equilibrium. Equilibrium is a concept that is central to later discussion.

Reactions like the ones described above are simple and, we might say, well-behaved. But more complicated reactions exist as well, where such things as stationary or oscillatory patterns of species may arise. A system is said to be chemically organized when more complicated behavior of reacting moieties, especially intermediates (such as described in Equation 3.4 above), is manifest. In fact, all chemically organized systems feature unusual behavior of intermediates.

System organization is quantified according to a measure of system disorder (technically, a thermodynamic measure called entropy). The lower a system's disorder, the higher is the degree of chemical organization. At the other extreme, a subject system achieves maximum disorder at equilibrium. Thus, high disorder is associated with equilibrium and low disorder is identified with chemical organization.

Left alone, all non-equilibrium systems tend to relentlessly approach equilibrium (the state of maximum disorder). The concept of equilibrium and the driving force toward such symmetry is key. The driving force toward equilibrium is related in a complex way to how far the system is from equilibrium. Thus, there is no driving force at equilibrium, whereas the driving force is large when the system exists in a state far from equilibrium.

Unless very small, changes that occur due to driving forces (reactions occurring away from equilibrium) are irreversible. Reactions happen in both directions. In a chemical reaction like that depicted in Equation 3.1 where reactant species [A] and [BC] react to form product species [AB] and [C], the reaction really proceeds in both directions. At equilibrium, the forward (by convention, reaction to the right) and the backward reaction occur at equal rates, and so the concentrations of all species remain the same over time. Note that equilibrium does not imply stasis, but rather an offsetting balance between competing actions. But if steps are taken to upset the balance, such as continually removing chemical species [A] or [BC] from the right hand side of Equation 3.1 as they form (thus minimizing the backward reaction by removing its reactants), then the overall reaction can be driven strongly in the forward direction. The resultant driving force is related to the difference between the new steady state concentrations of all four species compared to those found in the unperturbed equilibrium state.

It is imperative to understand whether a system is closed (isolated from the surrounding environment) or open. A closed system may in some way temporarily achieve a state far from equilibrium, and organize, but will become disorganized again as equilibrium is inevitably approached. Only in an open system (non-isolated), with a strong enough supply of energy to sustain the driving force, can chemical organization survive.

Several key examples will emphasize the key importance of these dry and laborious concepts to later discussion. One example is the earth, an open system. The large input of solar energy permits an opportunity for organization, but at the expense of concomitant earthbound decay and also the loss of heat energy radiated by the earth into space. An individual microbe, plant, animal or human is also an open system, totally dependent on outside energy sources to create and maintain intricate organization. So, in fact, is the human brain, the sole source of mental activity (the mind; see Chapter 5).

Note that all real-world processes involve inefficiencies, a common example being friction in mechanical systems. For this reason, the total energy spent on the creation and maintenance of organization is more (and often substantially so) than the energy content of the resultant organized material.

The last statement embodies the principles of the Second Law of Thermodynamics (the 'Second Law'). The Second Law states that the disorder of an isolated system (termed a closed system; one that does not exchange matter or energy with its surroundings) will spontaneously increase until a maximum of disorder is achieved at equilibrium.

In other words, according to the Second Law, left alone, systems will mix and randomize as much as possible. Warm things cool and cool things warm toward the temperature of the ambient environment, pressures tend to equalize within connected systems, and so forth. The tendency for systems to internally average out, or in other words, to achieve equilibrium, is the primary thrust of the Second Law.

Nevertheless, the Second Law notwithstanding, we see wondrous examples of astonishing structure all around us. This is true at all levels of organization, from the sub-microscopic and microscopic, through the middle dimensions which we experience directly, and in the cosmos at large. The problem is how to reconcile the observed, pervasive order with the ubiquitous forces of decay and dispersion inherent in the Second Law. On first blush, a spontaneously evolving universe seems to be impossible.

A Profound Clue about Order

So how can the universe sustain advances in complexity. Actually, the solution, in concept, is quite simple. The answer lies in the difference between closed and open systems.

The Belgian physicist Ilya Prigogine and others realized in the middle of the present century that the perceived hitch with the Second Law was the demand for a closed system. In the real world, systems are rarely closed, but rather usually exhibit energy in some form flowing in or out. If the flow of energy is strong enough, then the incessant decay ordained by the Second Law can be slowed, counterbalanced or reversed. The entire universe is a closed system, and so is inexorably running down. However, local pockets of order can form and grow, even in view of the Second Law. The secret to success is that, on balance, compensatory disorder must be perpetuated outside the local system of interest. In fact, the disorder will always at least slightly exceed the created order, due to inevitable inefficiencies.

An excellent example from common experience has been adapted from a description by Mitchell Waldrop in his book *Complexity*. Envision a pot of soup on a stove top burner. If the heat is off, then nothing happens, the soup sitting at room temperature equilibrium as predicted by the Second Law. If a small amount of heat is now continuously applied by low activation of the burner, then there is still not much happening of interest. The system (the pot of soup) is no longer quite at equilibrium, since heat energy rises through the soup from bottom to top. However, the temperature differences are small, and the process is little disturbed (it exists near to equilibrium, and is said to be well-behaved). But now consider the addition of a higher level of continuous heat, driving the system on average further from equilibrium. At some point, suddenly, instabilities arise due to the increased flux of heat energy. Random motions of molecules no longer average out, and some of the motions grow. Pockets of warmer liquid form and begin to rise, while some cooler pockets begin to fall. As the process continues, the motions tend to organize on a still larger scale. Under the right conditions, looking down on the soup surface from above reveals a pattern of convection cells, with fluid rising in the middle of each cell and falling along the sides. The soup has achieved the orderly process of simmering. The application of even stronger heat flux leads eventually to more turbulent boiling.

From where did the orderly state of simmering arise? The simmering is a pattern of activity that appeared in exactly the same group of soup molecules that were present prior to simmering. Simmering was induced by supplying energy (in this case, heat) from outside the system, such that the soup collectively contained more heat energy than it did at equilibrium (prior to turning on the burner). Given the right form and amount of energy, a new state of organization was achieved. And said state of organization can be sustained, and even permanently locked in, under the right circumstances. Basically, those circumstances are the availability of an ongoing supply of the right amount of energy to the subject system, to sustain the new organization. Relative to our example, we must continue to supply the correct amount of heat to sustain the simmering state in the pot of soup.

Science has recently begun to understand the dynamics of how organization and complexity can arise from a less organized state, given self-organizing interactions. Thus, we have discovered that innumerable physical systems, when left to themselves under the proper circumstances, can self-organize in startling ways. As one simple example, this approach explains in general how matter has progressively organized with time since the big bang to successively realize nuclear, atomic, and molecular entities, and how those entities have combined in countless ways to produce primordial dust and gas, stars, galaxies, planets and many other cosmic macro-entities. Further, self-organization reveals the general process (many details as yet unknown) of how the unprecedented intricacies of living material can arise from non-living material, and how simple, early living material could evolve to eventually realize higher life forms and even intelligence. For perspective, the fundamentals of self-organization have been found to pervade every discipline of science in important ways (e.g., see the many examples throughout the rest of the chapter). It appears that we have uncovered a profound clue regarding how the universe operates and advances.

The Key Role of Non-Linearity

To better understand the awesome potential of self-organization to produce surprising leaps of complexity, the notion of linearity versus non-linearity is crucial.

For perspective, physics historically assumed that cause and effect were proportionate in nature. If an increase in a given driving force for a system were doubled, then relevant system output was doubled. Hit a putt twice as hard and the golf ball will role twice as far. Or double the (relatively low) heat to a pot of soup and the state of simmering will be achieved in half the time. The magnitude of effect was considered to be directly in step with the applied causal influence.

Thus, most of nature was historically believed to follow a cozy, well-behaved plan of directly proportionate cause and effect. The large base of knowledge that existed principally consisted of systems studied near equilibrium, where virtually all systems are well behaved. In contrast, complexity was viewed as irritating irregularities that impeded the progress of knowledge. Complex systems were viewed as being strange merely because of our ignorance, and it was felt that such systems could be resolved into a set of simpler, well-behaved physical subsystems if we only knew how.

But the blind comfort of a well-behaved nature has recently been forever shattered. Currently, a completely new perspective is emerging, where irregularity and complexity are seen as the norm, and complex systems are understood as not simply the sum of simple, predictable parts. Complex systems do not show proportionate cause and effect. The result is that the sum of individual isolated parts does not reveal the behavior of the complex whole. In fact, often the behavior of the whole cannot be predicted from the performance of the individual parts at all. So the new system of thought argues that, to properly advance science, we must treat complexity as the fundamental reality, with simple, well-behaved systems becoming exceptions of special circumstance.

Another way to look at the old and the new is with reference to mathematical descriptions. In the historical view, the world was primarily populated by systems subject to linear mathematical description. For linear systems, the whole is equal to the sum of its parts, and so subsystems can be analyzed independently and then simply added together to predict behavior of the whole. In contrast, the new view purports that descriptions of all but the simplest real-world systems must be described using non-linear mathematics. For non-linear systems, the whole can be far more (or less) than the sum of its parts, and resolution into a set of additive subsystems is not possible. Furthermore, resultant system characteristics and behavior can be unexpected and, under our present limited knowledge, difficult to analyze.

Chaos - Why Prediction is Imperfect

Here we introduce yet another unusual property of matter. This will help add a better feel for the amazing intricacies of matter that confounds its full understanding.

As we shall see later in the chapter, the evolution of many dynamic systems is highly dependent on the initial conditions prior to process commencement, not just the relevant laws of nature (whether linear or non-linear) that govern the unfolding process. A common example would be the ballistic path of a baseball struck by a batter. At the instant of contact, we have a rough idea of the general trajectory of the baseball, due to visual and auditory clues. However, exact knowledge of the path and prediction of the precise point of contact with the ground is utterly out of the reach of modern science. Even the slightest variations in the contact point on the bat, bat velocity, angle of contact and point on the linear extent of the bat, and even tiny deviations in the localized mechanical properties of the bat and ball render true trajectory prediction far beyond the realm of possibility. Systems that are particularly dependent on initial conditions are formally labeled as chaotic systems.

Chaotic systems, especially when observed over the long term, behave in basically unpredictable and, for all practical purposes, random ways. Further, it seems that ordinary (non-chaotic) behavior is the exception, and virtually all dynamic systems are subject to chaos.

But it is crucial to note that the behavior of chaotic systems is not fundamentally indeterminate. On the contrary, it can be shown that the relevant initial conditions are sufficient to precisely set the entire future course of the system. The practical problem is when we attempt to set (or measure) the initial conditions of a real-world system. The baseball trajectory problem is a sterling example. There is always some degree of error in measurement, and so there is always uncertainty, no matter how slight. Even a nearly vanishing error can lead to huge uncertainties in the future behavior of chaotic systems. Thus, from a practical standpoint, the future course of the real world is wide open to unpredictable development.

So nature can, in principle, be both deterministic (subject to rigorous description) and yet random (produce results that cannot be predicted beforehand). In practice, therefore, determinism is not achievable. In the real world where non-linear, chaotic systems abound, the future cannot be predicted even with all the accessible facts at hand.

In review, our current understanding of the universe is largely dependent on the study of linear systems. But we now know that most systems of interest are non-linear and therefore often subject to disproportionate cause and effect. Although we don't yet have sufficient understanding, the day may come when we have a complete description of non-linear system dynamics. But we must also contend with chaos, and chaotic systems carry elements of unpredictability that seem insurmountable. Both non-linear and chaotic systems are deterministic, in the sense that if every minute detail were known then the system behavior would be completely determined forever. But the practical reality is that we cannot achieve full determinism in actual practice, due to fundamental limitations on our ability to measure or control all relevant circumstances.

The discovery that the realm of well-behaved, deterministic linearity is highly restricted is a profound finding. Even though the universe is subject to rigorous laws, new and unpredictable developments are the rule. No amount of information about the dynamic laws or initial conditions will permit the future to be known. Assuming that the dynamic natural laws are the only organizing forces controlling matter and energy, such propensity for undirected evolution (chaos coupled with the capacity of self-organization to lock-in and sustain new chemical and physical organization) is not possible in a strictly closed, linear, non-chaotic world. In turn, it would appear that the important processes in the universe we inhabit are open, non-linear, and chaotic, at least to some degree. The universe continues to evolve, and it is likely that new levels of even more advanced complexity are in store.

Why are the weighty concepts of this chapter important? Because the resultant, self-organizing scientific model of nature becomes highly similar to the nature that we actually experience. There is not the slightest shred of evidence that the universe we see today is the result of divine intervention or of preordained design. We also have extremely strong, independent lines of evidence that point to the big bang event, and therefore to a cosmic origin where the matter we see today was completely non-existent. Somehow the magnificent organization of matter that we observe now came to be automatically (through natural processes). And the latter train of thought also directly applies to the origin and evolution of life (yet a higher degree of matter's self-organization), since again, we see no evidence of divine tinkering or of the play out of a rigid design scheme, but we do see mounds of evidence for progressive spontaneous evolution. Finally, at least on earth, this process recently achieved the crowning event of earth-based evolution, the advent of human intelligence. We will speculate in Chapters 9 and 10 how the continued evolution of mind seems likely to bring the universe into a new era, one dominated by consciousness rather than by matter as we now experience.

Order, Organization, and Chaos

As mentioned earlier, many systems exhibit normal behavior under a spectrum of conditions, but may at some point encounter a threshold beyond which predictability breaks down. For example, the laminar flow in a pipe at low velocities becomes turbulent at some point as velocities are increased. Or the detailed design of a snowflake is determined only at the moment of crystallization, being a function of the absolute temperature, slight temperature gradients, the relative presence of dust and other particulates on which to condense, and so forth. In any case, a unique pathway for the system is no longer manifest. Rather the system can follow alternative scenarios, and new stages of organization may appear, many times bearing startling properties and complexity. Particularly interesting are cases where dynamic patterns of activity over space or time spontaneously appear (e.g., economics; weather; planet formation from a primordial, circumstellar disk of dust and gas), situations that compel a sense of collective cooperation by system elements. An additional clear example is the stripes of a tiger's coat, which form in part due to interacting gradients of independent diffusing chemical messengers in the embryo. Systems that enter and lock into such states are termed self-organizing.

Paradoxically, a profound outcome of the study of complex systems is that self-organization is often found closely aligned with chaos. As one critical illustration, precursors of biologically important molecules can be shown to properly combine into biologically significant form in the laboratory. The precursors must all reside in a watery soup featuring the proper ingredients and conditions, and suitable energy must be supplied to the system. When the situation is right, the random, chaotic interactions of the precursor molecules self-organize to form measurable amounts of many biologically important, more highly organized molecules. Another type of situation is represented by a stable array of interacting systems that suddenly get disturbed. The disturbance suddenly disrupts balance, and many or all elements must go through a complicated adaptation interval until balance is reestablished between all participating elements. Two examples of the latter situation would be an ecological niche where one member suddenly declined, or a company where a major player left.

Chaotic instability reigns until a new self-organized state of stability is re-established.

The fields of chaos and of self-organization are young and incomplete at present, and so an absolute tie is not yet at hand. However, the study of diverse systems leads to the strong intuitive sense that chaos frequently produces a necessary exploratory mode of gyrating system parameters that then, eventually and by chance, may encounter the proper conditions to settle into a stable, self-organized state.

Importantly, self-organized states are not random, but can usually be re-created, with regard to at least certain broad features, given the proper conditions. The simmering pot is an excellent example, since the state of simmering can be recreated over and over again given an appropriate sequence of alternating heat application and heat deprivation. Thus, in general, self-organized states must be viewed as a special class of emerging property inherent in the physical makeup (the matter) of the system constituents.

Insights from Feedback Theory

Open Loop Systems. A system may be diagrammed schematically as shown in Figure 3.1. For example, the system may be a car accelerator and engine combination with an output defined as car speed (Figure 3.1A). Formally, the main system functional element (termed the process in our example) is the car engine. The primary system input of consideration is accelerator position. The system, if it accomplishes any function, must also have one or more outputs. In our example, as mentioned, the output is car speed.

Manual control of car speed is effected by varying the depression of the accelerator pedal. Progressive pedal depression results in increased car speed. However, the relationship is not exact — for a given amount of accelerator depression, the speed may be relatively fast, medium or slow depending on such variables as road surface and slope and also car weight and load. The engine does not 'know' what effect its action is having relative to desired outcome, but merely burns fuel at a fixed rate for a given accelerator position. The system is said to lack feedback (ignoring the driver), because some measure of the ultimate system function, car speed, is not 'fed back' to influence engine action. Systems without feedback are also termed open loop, because no measure of actual system outcome is 'looped back' to control system action.

Closed Loop Systems. Of more interest here are closed loop (feedback) control systems. A logical extension of the open loop car speed control system above is the cruise control option. Functionally and diagrammatically, the closed loop cruise control is more complicated (Figure 3.1B) than the simple accelerator-driven system. The main system functional element (the process) is still the

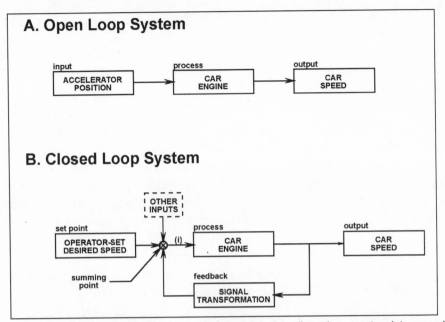

A. Open Loop System

input → ACCELERATOR POSITION → process → CAR ENGINE → output → CAR SPEED

B. Closed Loop System

OTHER INPUTS

set point → OPERATOR-SET DESIRED SPEED → (i) → process → CAR ENGINE → output → CAR SPEED

summing point

feedback → SIGNAL TRANSFORMATION

Figure 3.1 Control systems theory can be envisioned as dissecting a system into several distinct components, depending upon the type of control. Here we treat two simple types of control system, open loop and closed loop.

(A) Open Loop Systems. A basic open loop system can be modeled around a central process, the car engine as discussed in the main text, that is responsible for the ultimate system output, in our example, car speed. An open loop system also typically has some input, in the present illustration, accelerator position. For an open loop system, the output is purely a function of the input signal to the process, there being no monitoring of output to verify desired performance.

(B) Closed Loop Systems. A rudimentary closed loop system can be formed by providing feedback of system output to control the central process. In the figure, the output is sampled, and the resultant signal is analyzed to produce an appropriate index of the system output for conveyance to the processor. Actually, the feedback signal is first compared to (more specifically, subtracted from) a set point signal (a measure that defines the specific output desired) at a 'summing point' located prior to presentation of data to the processor. (Other signals, perhaps relaying the needs of distinct interrelated systems, could be introduced at the summing point as well.) Thus, in a closed loop control system, the signal that drives the processor is representative not of merely an uncontrolled input (as with an open loop control system), but of the difference between actual and desired behavior. The overall system is designed to constantly drive the immediate processor input signal (i) to zero (so that no discrepancy exists between desired and actual output).

engine, being the ultimate source of output (car speed). However, the primary input is not accelerator position, but rather some measured function of car speed. Thus, the system is directly sensing some index of the desired outcome and is controlling the system process to converge on the desired output, in this case, car speed.

The main system process is 'told' the target speed by virtue of a signal or setting called the 'set point.' For a car cruise control, the set point represents the constant value (setting) chosen by the driver as the desired speed. However, more generally, the set point might be established by various measurements and computations relative to the subject system or be determined in some complex way by one or more additional interacting systems.

Positive and Negative Feedback. In general, feedback can be of two kinds, positive or negative. Our example of a vehicle cruise control represents negative feedback. In negative feedback, small deviations from the target behavior are made to die away (are negated). The system always attempts to maintain the difference between the feedback signal and the set point at zero, so that system output will be identical with the set point.

Alternatively, positive feedback is characterized by the tendency for small deviations to become magnified. For instance, placing a microphone too close to a loudspeaker causes a screeching sound due to runaway amplification (the amplified sound from the loudspeaker becomes a new input to the microphone, and the system then amplifies that sound further, which is then picked up by the microphone and amplified again, and so forth *ad infinitum*. This is exactly what happens in spontaneous self-organization, some minor and usually random fluctuation resulting in perhaps catastrophic change. Thus, in mathematical terms, the dependence of self-organization on self-reinforcement is admirably represented by positive feedback.

In a sense, the Second Law exerts a negative feedback influence on spontaneous organization in nature. Any chance locus of transient sporadic organization is immediately attacked by incessant tendencies to reestablish disorder. As an example, a cloud formation that happens to remind a viewer of some object is usually lost rather quickly due to incessant formation, random movement and dissolution of the individual elements that form the cloud's global appearance. On the other hand, spontaneous self-organization is the direct result, under proper circumstances, of the runaway enhancement (positive feedback) of small, random perturbations. The formation of diamonds (extended arrays of spontaneously formed carbon crystals) from highly compressed underground petroleum moieties are a good example. The particular chaotic influence of impurities and details of formation render each diamond with a unique signature that is permanently encrusted in the crystal lattice.

While diamonds illuminate an interesting exception due to remarkable stability, the newly self-organized form is usually subject to incessant attack. Once formed, any new locus of self-organization must typically be constantly protected from subsequent decay (related to the Second Law) by a continuing expenditure of energy to maintain the special organized state. Diamonds are a rare exception, but for most self-organizing systems such as simmering pots of soup, ecological niches and reconfigured companies, energy must be actively supplied on an endless basis for the integrity of the new organized form to persist.

Examples of Self-Organization

On the surface, it seems counter intuitive that the capacity for self-organization appears to arise from chaos. But in fact, as we have seen, chaotic systems often seem prerequisite to self-organized systems in nature. Chaos and organization are opposites from one view, but are harmonious from another. The dynamics of physical systems existing far from equilibrium reveal the emerging property of chaos, and, under the proper circumstances, self-organization. As described earlier, it seems as though chaos provides critical 'exploration' to 'find' the proper conditions allowing self-organization to materialize.

Self-organization is absolutely fundamental to the entire theme of this book. Thus, to facilitate improved understanding, the following discussion presents several examples where chaotic principles are applied to real-world situations.

Sand Piles. A well-known model of chaotic self-organization is the simple pile of sand. Some have simulated the dynamics of sand piles experimentally, and others have created computer models. Importantly, both methods lead to the same general conclusions.

We will describe here the experimental approach employed by Glenn Held and colleagues at the IBM Thomas J. Watson Research Center. The latter group designed an apparatus that pours sand, one grain at a time, onto a small, flat, circular surface. Upon initiating the process, the first few grains come to rest directly on the surface near the point of impact. Continued pouring results in the progressive buildup of a small mound with gentle slopes. In this fashion, as more sand is added, the pile continues to grow, achieving increased height and spreading laterally to the edge of the circular surface.

From time to time, the slope in a local area becomes too steep, and some grains slide down the incline in a small avalanche. As the pile enlarges, steep inclines are more common and typical avalanches grow larger.

Careful study of the details of avalanche formation reveal important facts illuminating to our overall discussion. Any avalanche starts with one grain beginning to slide down the pile surface. The pioneering grain had become unstable, and was no longer supported sufficiently by surrounding grains. The breakaway grain will continue falling until a new condition of stability is achieved. As the grain slides, it may nudge other grains that are teetering on instability, and they may fall as well. In turn, the secondary falling grains may elicit tertiary grains to fall, and so forth. The avalanche will continue until all grains have either reached a new position of stability or have fallen off of the circular surface.

Once formed, and given the continued addition of more sand, the pile maintains an average shape and size dictated by the diameter of the flat surface. A balance exists over time between particles added and those falling off the surface. The latter situation is termed the 'critical state.' When the pile is initially forming, the slope of the pile is subcritical, avalanches are small and less frequent, and the pile continues to grow. But once the critical state has been achieved, if the pile momentarily develops a steeper than critical slope, the average size of avalanches is found to grow larger and more frequent, until the pile is reduced once again to the critical state. Notice then, that, once formed, the critical state is self-perpetuating.

By observing a small area of the pile, it is possible to declare when the next small avalanche is likely. Nevertheless, the exact point and time of a small avalanche cannot be predicted with certainty. But in addition, much larger avalanches are not possible to anticipate through local observation at all, because they are due to the global history and state of the entire pile. Regardless of the local dynamics, the average size and frequency of large avalanches is a holistic characteristic of the overall pile. The result is a chaotic, self-organized system that is unpredictable instant by instant but that exhibits a remarkably persistent critical state over time.

Economics. Let's now turn from beach dynamics to focus on a particular social behavior of beings who populate some beaches. Modern, classical economics is the direct descendent of economics taught decades ago. Little has changed in the basic tenets. Classical economics teaches that small changes in a system tend to die away. The fundamental underlying principle is that of diminishing returns, the concept that too much of a good thing is not good. Examples include the problems encountered when we or our businesses overspend, overextend, or overindulge. The more a person or entity does something, a point is reached where added increments are less and less beneficial.

The above story has a familiar ring. The muffling of small changes is exactly what we encountered in feedback control theory. Traditional economics resembles negative feedback, just like a car cruise control where any change of speed from the set point is immediately counteracted. In the same way that negative feedback suppresses small changes, thereby stabilizing physical systems and protecting them from runaway behavior, diminishing returns constrain products or firms from growing so large that the market is forever totally controlled. Buyers are fickle, the story goes. Once a competitor produces products or services superior in some fashion, the loyalty of many consumers will shift to the new source.

Classical economics further extends the argument of diminishing returns beyond individual markets to attempt an explanation of all economic balance and solidarity. Furthermore, the classical economic model purports that situations not subject to diminishing returns (not dependent on negative feedback) are unusual and are of little consequence to general understanding. The philosophy also states that the law of diminishing returns acts to operate the market in a fashion that sorts out the best products and services for success and endurance.

That is the classic model of economics. But is the real-world actually like this? For some well-behaved markets, during stable periods, perhaps. However, striking examples exist of tumultuous times (e.g., the great depression; recurrent recessions, etc.) or of bizarre behavior in certain markets. As a simple example, major industries exist where dominance by one or a few players can be readily identified. Prominent archetypes include the software, soft drink, cereal, bus, and commercial truck industries and also the major television networks. Such industries feature a small number of huge organizations that control the sales, often in active and sometimes ruthless ways that make legitimate competition unlikely or virtually impossible.

There are, in addition, intriguing illustrations of poor products or services becoming industry wide standards. Such instances loudly dispute the traditional economic model where poor products are expected to be snuffed out through declining sales (diminishing returns). The conventional QWERTY keyboard layout (an abbreviation that designates the normal keyboard arrangement) used by virtually all typewriters and computers can serve as a product-related illustration. The QWERTY keyboard layout was originally designed to include intentional inefficiency, to slow typists down so that they wouldn't type too fast on the original (late nineteenth century) sluggish typewriters. Nevertheless, marketplace flukes led to a spurt of initial sales, and then serendipitous circumstances of the times led other competitors to jump on the bandwagon. The result is that the QWERTY design endured past the era of typewriter inefficiency. Thus, throughout this century, the inefficient QWERTY keyboard layout has enjoyed a virtual monopoly.

As another example, the American car industry arrogantly resisted sensible car sizes, economic fuel consumption, and aggressive quality control for an extended period, until Japanese competition finally forced U.S. producers to comply with what a large segment of the populace obviously wanted. Poor products often win, at least for extended periods, in direct conflict with the tenets of classical economics.

So we see that phenomena such as increasing (as opposed to decreasing) returns, lock-in behavior, unpredictability, and tiny events having enormous evolutionary consequences, are all readily observed in real-world economics. This is the stuff of positive feedback, and brings the study of economics directly into the world of self-organizing complexity.

Some people are now seriously studying how increasing returns can co-exist with decreasing returns to explain modern economics. Also, traditional theory regarded all people as identical, whereas the new self-organizing approach views individuals as distinctly behaving entities. In this way, the old theme of equal potentiality becomes replaced with the notion that differences and happenstance can act as potent driving forces. Finally, the historical concept was one of relative stasis (no real dynamics), whereas the new approach is built around a vibrant yet indeterminate dynamic, living on the edge of chaos with structure often in a fitful state of exploratory wandering until conditions trigger a new self-organized collective behavior. In short, the old economics was founded on a simple model of stability, equilibrium, and determinism, while the new economics is characterized by inherently complex patterns of activity and indeterminable, chaotically-driven, self-organization.

It is important to mention that the new vision of economics is embryonic and controversial. It is not known how the relative roles of the classical and new economic theories will shake out over time. The point here is to show how the principles of chaotic, self-organizing systems can offer insightful perspective not only in the dusty archives of science, but also in our world of direct experience.

Weather. Another common example of chaotic systems at work is predicting the weather. Earth's atmospheric system is extremely complicated, chaotic, replete with numerous examples of self-organized systems (low and high pressure systems; warm and cold fronts; hurricanes and cyclones; etc.), and can be predicted with accuracy only over very short periods of time. However, by recognizing the subject system as chaotic, progress has been made in understanding some of the basic underlying characteristics. It is the goal to develop mathematical descriptions that, coupled with the ongoing input of better real-world data, will allow much more extended specification of the probability distribution of allowed events in the future. Given such an achievement, for example, it might be possible to predict at least the general weather several weeks from today.

Evolution of Earth Life. Finally, a stunning example of chaos coupled with self-organization is the evolution of life on earth.

If evolution were deterministic, then the laws of nature would inherently hold an explicit recipe for every catastrophe and ecological niche throughout the history of the earth. Nature, however, economizes in a fascinating and beautiful way. Rather than storing and playing out a preordained record, the evidence suggests that the richness of possibilities inherent in chaos is used to tap and trap happenstance. Thus, eventually, through random chaotic exploration and the capture of interesting forms through self-organization, virtually every approach to solving a given evolutionary problem gets tested, in one form or another. The exact approach and solution are not at all predestined in any way or to any extent. However, through relentless blind trial and error, virtually all general approaches get their chance at the plate.

In the theme of the present discussion then, evolution can be seen to work as follows. Random mutations and chance circumstances combine to chaotically provide diversity, both within and between species and through the creation of new species. Then, the process of natural selection tests the resulting candidates for the best functionality through continual exposure to real-world situations. On average, those members of a species that perform better also reproduce more efficiently. Eventually, new traits infiltrate the entire population to a progressively greater extent according to the relative advantages afforded.

Thus, earth life can be used as a clear illustration of several concepts introduced in this chapter:

- **The Second Law.** A living being requires an ongoing input of energy to survive (to maintain the self-organized state). Once the outside source of energy is permanently cut off, the being dies (loses it's ability to carry out the physical and metabolic steps necessary to prevent decay of the self-organized state);
- **Open System**. Earth life is an open system, because it depends on energy inputs from outside the system boundaries (outside the external envelope of the living entity or collection of entities). Organized processes in a closed system must inevitably run down for lack of a driving force (the energy from outside the system);
- **Equilibrium**. For the living, equilibrium means death. Life directly depends on the active maintenance of a self-organized state. Self-organized states typically exist far from equilibrium, and so require a continual input of energy to prevent decay of the system to equilibrium, as dictated by the Second Law;
- **Linearity and Feedback**. As an example of higher life forms, the human body is a gargantuan and intricate machine from a control theory standpoint. Virtually all of the thousands of chemical reactions which constitute the metabolic actions of our cells and also the communications systems of the body involve negative feedback (set point) control, and many of the reaction systems are distinctly non-linear. Some positive (runaway) feedback is evident as well, as seen in the processes of sneezing, coughing, vomiting and sexual orgasm. Our bodies and our world are decidedly non-linear and pervaded by interlaced feedback control systems;
- **Chaos**. The origin and evolution of both matter and of life fundamentally spring from the incessant chaotic interaction of molecules and of

existing organized entities. While some self-organization of matter would occur in the absence of chaos, the bizarre behavior of many matter forms when chaotically driven far from equilibrium instills the universe with the potential for tremendous extra organization. Yet, this is only true if such extraordinary organization can somehow be permanently captured. This leads to the final point:

- **Organization and Chaos**. The mindless, chaotic attributes of matter systems driven far from equilibrium are the mainstay of self-organization. Occasionally, the right conditions arise through chaos for new organized forms to come into being. And if the right energy sources are also available, the new organized form may be transient or even permanently captured and sustained.

The above points are not at all limited to life on earth, but pervade the entire physical world as we understand it today. We truly live in a cosmos that is characterized by far-from-equilibrium self-organization that is typified by open, non-linear and chaotic systems, and that is also highly interlaced with feedback and universally subject to the Second Law. The latter attributes are assumed when references are made to self-organizing systems or to self-organization in the rest of the book.

For completeness, it should be noted that self-organizing systems can form not only in the far-from-equilibrium realm, but also in the near-equilibrium arena. The equilibrium and non-equilibrium realms are quite distinct, however, relative to the nature of new formed complexity. In the equilibrium arena, the resulting state is comparatively static and inactive (such as the sand pile discussed previously). In contrast, self-organized states that originate far from equilibrium tend to be dynamic, being dependent on and animated through the need for substantial throughput of energy and matter recruited from the system's environment (e.g., earth life; weather; economics). The result is more reminiscent of a process than a state.

The Game of Life

The above discussion has shown a glimpse of how simple local processes might lead on occasion to elaborate global patterns. An important extension of the latter concept can be derived from a peek at what is termed cellular automata theory.

Cellular automata theory was originally introduced by John Von Neumann and Stanislaw Ulam as a mathematical model for self-reproduction in living systems. Since then, the details of cellular automata have been explored by a wealth of investigators in diverse fields of science.

A cellular automata is composed of a rectilinear array of square cells (like a checker board). Typically, cellular automata are modeled as having a very large number of cells, usually being infinite in extent. Most investigators have studied cellular automata of one or two dimensions, but higher dimensionalities have also been explored.

Cellular automata work according to a small set of elementary rules. We will consider automata where a given cell is either occupied or is empty (denoted, respectively, by '1' and '0'). To illustrate how a one dimensional automaton (a single row of cells) works, simple rules are assigned to govern all behavior. For example, to begin a new cycle, assume that each cell is assigned a value '0' if the two immediately adjacent cells (one left and one right) are either both occupied or both empty, or the value '1' if either the right or left adjacent cell (but not both) is occupied. To 'play' the automaton, one defines an initial pattern of occupied and empty cells, and then proceeds to apply the rule sequentially to every cell in the automaton to create the pattern for the next cycle. Cycles can be repeated indefinitely, and the outcome is completely deterministic (assuming the rules have no ambiguity). The term automaton comes from the automatic and predetermined nature of system evolution.

Cellular automata of various dimensions exhibit common features of behavior. As mentioned, automata are governed by simple, unambiguous rules, being transformed to the pattern for the next cycle strictly according to the local pattern of the present cycle. The only other variable is the initial conditions, the pattern of cell occupancy defined prior to execution of the first cycle of the series.

Remarkably, some cellular automata can lead to the spontaneous creation of complex patterns characterized by long-range order. Steven Wolfram finds that, in general, for one-dimensional automata, four growth patterns are evident. The beginning pattern may be lost, grow continuously, grow and then shrink, or grow to a particular level and then stabilize.

Two-dimensional automata are even more bewitching, in many cases exhibiting properties of elaborate self-organization. Examples include the development of 'structures' (enduring features resulting from cell patterns), periodic (repeating) phenomena, organized structures that move, and even self-reproduction of features that then endure and, in some cases, eventually reproduce again and again. In general, different initial conditions result in distinct outcomes. However, for a defined set of rules, the general nature of the observed results is often reasonably similar over a broad spectrum of initial conditions. In turn, as the rules are changed substantially, the general behavior typically changes as well.

Cellular automata have been found to closely resemble self-organizing structures from the real world. For both, the processes are irreversible in time. This means that recent events cannot be undone without forcefully altering the process at hand. Also, self-organizing processes define a direction to time, always moving forward. In contrast, the observation of systems at equilibrium provides no clue to the direction of time. At equilibrium, changes proceed in the forward and backward directions at an equal rate, and any analysis of molecular motions or other mechanisms is totally symmetrical and is devoid of any information about time direction. The lack of a sense of time has been a major, long-standing weakness of classical (equilibrium) physics.

One class of cellular automata has been called the Game of Life, first introduced in 1970 by mathematician John Conway. The initial game and most subsequent versions are represented by two-dimensional arrays of cells where each cell is marked as being alive or dead. As usual for any automaton, initial conditions are set, rules are defined, and the automaton is run through successive cycles to observe the resultant patterns. Each cycle is called a generation. In general, the rules dictate that, for any cell in a given generation, a review is made of the immediate neighbors (for a two-dimensional grid, there are eight neighbors, counting cells contacted at the corners). If many neighbors are alive (the exact number being specified in the rules), then the subject cell dies before the next generation due to overcrowding. Alternatively, if too few neighbors are alive, the cell will die of loneliness before the next generation. Finally, if the number of neighbors is just right, the cell is alive for the next generation, either due to survival (if already occupied) or by being born (if the cell was empty before).

Given the right initial conditions, a display of the results in checkerboard fashion on a computer screen reveals a vibrant scene that mimics life in many ways. Intensive study of the Game Of Life automaton by innumerable workers has revealed, under the right circumstances, structures that form, move in an organized fashion, reproduce, attack other structures, undergo life cycles, and other behaviors reminiscent of organic life as known on earth.

One group that has conducted detailed studies of the Game of Life is Per Bak and colleagues. The latter workers have carefully analyzed the results of intentionally introduced perturbations into automata that had otherwise stabilized in some particular pattern of behavior. The results indicate that the system would generally undergo transient disturbances of varying and unpredictable magnitude, but would eventually return to the unperturbed pattern of activity.

This inherent stability and resiliency to perturbations is significant. The systems meet the primary properties of a self-organized critical state, such as the sand pile discussed earlier in this chapter. In addition, the collective distribution of births and deaths after perturbations followed a power law consistent with one well-known type of formal chaotic behavior. Under further investigation, the correspondence with chaos proved to be quite general. The basic outcome was robust in the face of wide changes in game rules, including the spontaneous addition of organisms, intentional weighting of organisms in particular areas, and extension to three-dimensional models. All variations evolved to a critical state, and were subject to description by mathematical laws consistent with chaotic processes.

The importance of the latter result is that, as described above, the Game of Life mimics real-world life in many ways. The study of the Game of Life is directed in part to see exactly how far the models resemble real life, and to what extent insights about life's origin and advancement can be learned from the models. At least based on the studies to date, life seems to be, in some eerie way, mathematical in character. But perhaps we shouldn't be so surprised. We will see later that the entire universe seems to have a mysterious, spooky connection to mathematics that we don't as yet understand.

The Game of Real Life

We humans find ourselves in a game of (organic) life that is for real. In an intriguing, wondrous sort of way, our situation mimics broad aspects of the cellular automaton counterpart. In fact, we shall see that our organic life is self-organizing. Furthermore, like the automaton, evolution builds on what is already at hand rather than employing fresh designs for new systems. Thus, organic life's emerging structures are not preordained. Quite the contrary, diverse potential solutions develop through chaotic happenstance, are locked in through self-organization, and then are evaluated for fitness through natural selection.

We will also find that the universe is a chaotic, self-organizing system. This profound discovery of the twentieth century means that the universe too must make do with what is available, and that the ultimate outcome is not cast in some world blueprint. If the laws of mechanics exert the only governing controls of energy and matter, then the future of the universe is in principle unknowable. No finite intelligence, regardless of extent or depth, could predict the patterns or systems that will emerge as time further unfolds.

As we peer out deep into the cosmos, everything we see appears to be governed by precisely the same natural laws that we find near home. Countless examples could be sighted, but the most prominent are that the four forces of nature (gravity; electromagnetism; the strong nuclear force; the weak nuclear force) have exactly the same values everywhere, as far as we can tell today. Everything else follows from the four forces, so that all of physics, chemistry, biology and every other discipline would also be expected to be the same everywhere. And, in fact, no exceptions have ever been found.

Furthermore, even if the odds are quite low, conditions similar to earth's are likely to exist in many other places in the vast universe. Given the stupendous self-organizing nature of nature, it is inconceivable that we are alone in the cosmos and that this grand universal landscape that we view is sterile and solely for our visual amusement.

Mankind has always displayed an insatiable quest for god and a better understanding of the cosmos and our existence therein. We do not yet know whether god can be explained naturally or if circumvention of natural laws is required. In either case, the very existence of evolved life provides powerful evidence for some purpose to the universe.

But what is this strange condition called life? It is to this elusive subject that we now direct the discussion.

Chapter 4
The Astounding Essence of Life

The Role of Self-Organization

What is Life? On first blush, this seems like a trivial question. The average person feels that the recognition of (our form of earthbound organic) life is easy. Even if asked to write a definition of life, most people would probably head for a biology book and cite an impressive list of properties that would agree with most other general references.

But, in the final analysis, things aren't so simple. In fact, it is not elementary in all cases to define what is living and what is not. Also, there is no known single characteristic that is unique to life. Finally, we are entrained by the nature of life on earth, the only life we know, a trap that may prove misleading. The latter issues are critical, and each is explored immediately below to aid orientation:

Bounds. Organic life forms composed of one or more cells can be labeled as living in most cases without eliciting controversy. The only instances where questions arise relate to some states of cells where animation is suspended and a dormant episode ensues to the point where inspection proves ambiguous (e.g., certain spores, etc.). However, outside of the realm of typical multi-cellular and single celled organisms, debate, sometimes vigorous, rises to the forefront;

Properties. The standard attributes normally associated with organic life, such as reproduction, complexity, growth, adaptability, respiration, etc., are exhibited in one fashion or another by many physical and chemical systems that no one would classify as living. We must therefore look beyond a mere list of properties to define life; and

Focus. The study of living forms on earth certainly is relevant to understanding aspects of organic life in an earth-based context. But great care is warranted. Until we better comprehend the true scope of life in the universe, conclusions must be cautious and guarded.

Much more will be said about such fundamental issues in the present chapter and in the remainder of the book.

As discussed in more detail below, a very strong consensus of relevant scientists believes that life evolved on earth from non-living material. Accepting the majority view, living organisms are therefore a stunning testament to emerging properties and self-organization. Furthermore, humans embody the pinnacle of such accomplishment, on earth at least. As mentioned previously, the human brain, a spectacular result of living systems, is the most complex system in the known universe.

Since earth bound forms are the only life we know, the terrestrial biosphere will of necessity occupy our attention. The goal is to examine what is known about life, to set the stage for discussions in later chapters regarding mind and its relation to the universe. And acquiescing to the old adage, the place to start is at the beginning.

The Birth and Advancement of Life

Life began on earth a long time in the past. The earliest evidence places the beginning of single-celled earth life about 3.8 billion years ago.

The age of the earth is estimated to be on the order of 4.6 billion years. Importantly, earth's early bombardment by meteorites and also internally-trapped heat from earth's formation created surface temperatures considered too hot for life to form until about 4.0 billion years ago. Thus, it would seem that life had to form, evolve through all required pre-cellular steps, and also invent cells within 200 million years (4.0 - 3.8 billion years). This is truly an astonishing rate of development. The upshot is that, in the perspective of geologic time, life evolved almost instantly, once conditions were acceptable.

The earth's surface is dynamic when viewed over geological time. Hardly any undisturbed evidence remains from the time when life began. However, a few tantalizing tidbits of data have been uncovered. Coupled with a large amount of laboratory experimentation and comparative analysis with known systems of more recent vintage, we can gain a surprising glimmer of our heritage.

Life now evolves through processes occurring in well-established living systems. That could not have been the case when life first formed. Most probably, life arose through a progressive series of pre-cellular stages to finally achieve something we would unambiguously identify as alive today. The first few phases were undoubtedly far from living, but certainly must have been organized. As the complexity of relevant systems grew, the properties and behavior would probably, quite slowly and successively, have assumed more and more life-like characteristics. Thus, the threshold of life may have been considerably blurred.

It is critical to realize that living organisms can be completely specified at the level of atoms and molecules. For one, there is not the slightest hint that any extra-molecular vital force or essence accompanies life. Also, no information would be added by attempting to specify further detail, say, with reference to the subatomic world. So, the domain of life is that of atoms and molecules, and the domain of atoms and molecules is that of chemistry. In fact, earth life is most fundamentally a problem of organic chemistry (the chemistry of carbon and its compounds).

All living things on earth are based on organic chemistry. Organic compounds, especially moieties with much complexity, are usually not stable for extended periods of time at earth surface temperatures. For such temperatures, all molecules constantly twist and turn incessantly, and the resultant stresses and strains eventually break down interesting organic molecules. So the odds of finding organic molecule fossils (primary fossils, remains of the actual organism) in substantial quantities is quite poor. Minerals are more enduring, and, although rare, some mineralized fossils from primordial epochs have been found. Such secondary fossils (ones that are replicas rather than original living material) represent a locus once occupied by an organism where minerals infiltrated and bonded to mimic some of the form of the initial being.

It is puzzling that, reviewing the entire evolutionary span as a whole, we confront a surprising finding. Once cells had undergone their rapid appearance, the simplest single-celled organisms appear to have taken the longest time to evolve, compared to later multi-cellular stages. Consider the following facts. As mentioned, the earliest record of single celled organisms indicates an origin about 3.8 billion years ago. In turn, the first evidence of multi-cellular organisms suggests that the most remote are roughly 1.4 billion years old, more than 2 billion years later. Finally, the conventional (primary) fossil record appears about 0.6 billion years ago. The primary fossil record relates to beings with hard parts that have been preserved directly. As beings have become more complex, the pace of change has paradoxically accelerated.

It is interesting that pre-cellular evolution is usually informally taught to be the big hurdle. Remarkably, though, pre-cellular evolution seems to have happened within a geologic flash. In contrast, notice that the interval featuring only single-celled life exceeds two billion years, implying that the leap from single-celled organisms to beings with multiple cells was a particularly formidable obstacle. Finally, once multi-cellular organisms arose, the evolutionary pace was greatly invigorated. As an example, mammals have only existed for the last 200 million years (0.2 billion years), and have only really prospered during the most recent 60 million years.

Biochemical Evolution

The properties of molecules are solely determined by their constituent atoms. Furthermore, a remarkably limited constellation of molecular types form the foundation for life as known on earth.

The biochemical evolution of life is usually discussed in terms of the 'primordial soup' of earth's early oceans. The latter metaphor means it is assumed that some group of pre-life molecules formed through random molecular assembly processes in primitive water systems (the ocean edges; tidal pools; lakes) of the young earth. The process may also have been aided by heat sources such as hot springs and volcanoes, and probably by the circulation of small organic molecules into various layers of the atmosphere where energetic ultra-violet light could propel otherwise improbable reactions and transformations. Note that if pre-cellular life really evolved and was sustained under very hot conditions, then the actual origin may have occurred somewhat earlier than our assumed 4.0 billion years.

There is reason to believe that the primordial soup eventually contained a rich brew of innumerable organic molecules, some of surprising complexity, among many other constituents. The scene was that of continuous, random, probing interaction on a grand scale, virtually every combination being eventually tested countless times through mindless chance encounters.

What is fascinating is that only a few molecular classes survived the global blending pot to play a pivotal role in emerging life. The list of major organic molecular classes for all of earthbound life is very short, being limited to nucleic acids, proteins, carbohydrates, lipids, and selected composites of the four listed building blocks. This astounding conclusion means that living material from every minuscule corner of all of the earth, throughout the entire tenure of life on the planet, centers on only four fundamental categories of molecules. The latter four classes will be termed the molecules of life.

Why were so few molecular classes selected in the ruthless struggles of the primordial soup? Because each of the winning molecule categories must have done something very, very well, apparently better than the primordial competition. Then, once the early self-organized molecular classes gained a slight foothold, an important competitive advantage was apparently enjoyed relative to stability, raw materials supply, chemistry, and other parameters that promoted survival. Subsequently, over mind-bending eons of time, more and more complex molecules and eventually systems of molecules emerged, sporting successively improved and efficient security and endurance compared to less robust primal ancestors.

The pathway of pre-life biochemical evolution may have been quite contorted. As an illustration, the invention of genes most assuredly involved far more than a chance linear assembly of nucleotides. It is probable that many otherwise strange and unlikely states happened to form in just the right way and at just the right time, creating a staging ground to unsystematically aid the ultimate reactions of interest to proceed. Thus, we expect that most likely the development followed a random, illogical, roundabout course not at all pre-destined to achieve the particular end result that materialized. If the true pathway of biochemical evolution were ever to become known, we would probably be flabbergasted at the mindless, contorted course and gross inefficiency of the route — the actual trajectory is almost assuredly nothing like an evolutionary engineer would have designed. We will see the latter theme popping up throughout this book. Nature makes do with what is available at the time, not what is the most logical.

To reiterate, the molecules of life are absolutely crucial, forming not only the structure of life but actually serving to define and characterize life. Furthermore, the molecules of life are not found at all (on earth) where there is no life. And, as mentioned, humans share the same general biochemistry with every life form on earth, from the lowly blue green algae, through amoebae, insects, the entire plant kingdom, and everything else that is alive. The brotherhood of life is an exceedingly select group.

It is clear that the molecules of life are marvelously specialized for a panoply of diverse and intricate functions. A brief summary will provide important perspective:

Nucleic Acids. For bacteria, plants, animals, and in fact for all entities where there is no controversy about the existence of organic life, all reproduction of any kind involves nucleic acids. Furthermore, the nucleic acids are all organized as genes, bead-like strings of individual nucleic acids (and, in most cases, other enveloping components) that encode an exquisitely precise blueprint for replication and function;

Carbohydrates. This class of organic molecules is most commonly associated with immediate or readily accessible energy, since carbohydrates can be quickly broken down (metabolized) to produce energy-laden molecular species directly useful in other reactions; but carbohydrates have also been recruited to serve as structural elements, molecular docking points, sensors, and in intracellular (within the cell) and intercellular (between cells) communications functions; finally, the carbohydrates are the ultimate source of all food on earth; by trapping energy from sunlight through the process of photosynthesis, plants fabricate carbohydrates from the simple raw materials of carbon dioxide and water; in turn, every other living thing, directly or indirectly, eats the resultant carbohydrates;

Lipids. Such compounds are ubiquitous to membranes, which in turn serve to isolate cells from the external environment and to compartmentalize cells and sub-cellular structures; attached to or imbedded in membranes are much of the machinery of the cell, where most of the really critical activities can be more precisely controlled and executed in a highly orchestrated fashion; lipids also form the basis of many hormones and other communicating moieties, and, as fat, represent the most concentrated form of energy storage; and

Proteins. Many proteins are superb building blocks in animals, forming structure and framework for other activities; key examples include membranes, hair, teeth, fingernails, muscle, tendons, microtubules (internal structural framework of cells), and many more; proteins also serve as animal and plant enzymes, incredible organic catalysts that provide tremendous facilitation and control for chemical reactions that otherwise would be quite inefficient or useless in the range of terrestrial and body temperatures.

The above-listed molecules of life also join in various combinations to form important composite molecular classes, such as lipopolysaccharides (lipid and carbohydrate compounds), lipoproteins (lipid and protein amalgamations), and mucopolysaccharides (carbohydrate and protein combinations). Importantly, even though there are only four main molecular classes, the numbers of individual molecular species in each class are very large. Furthermore, the farther apart living forms appear on life's evolutionary tree, the more different the individual moieties of the constellation of molecular species may be.

As we shall see, virtually all important life that we now know is based on cells. The path through pre-cellular biochemical evolution certainly had to derive certain key features common to cells along the way. The molecules of life are one hurdle for sure. Also essential was the development and recruitment of enzymes. Earlier discussion related the critical role enzymes play in controlling selected chemical reactions and allowing them to proceed under ambient as opposed to laboratory conditions. The development of enzymes would have permitted organized but primitive systems to make raw materials that were not available in the immediate environment. Still another essential skill necessarily acquired at some point was the storage of energy until needed for a controlled reaction, circumventing the previous necessity to happen on an energy source at just the right time to carry out a key reaction.

In addition, the birth of primitive membranes, perhaps initially unrecognizable as such, would have been critical to help create special protected environments for reactions and to arrange primitive assembly lines for reaction cascades. The list could go on and on. The point is that, to build complexity, countless molecular systems (combinations of two or more molecules) must have been randomly tested, and a vanishingly small number proved particularly advantageous relative to survival and replication. Then, such advanced systems interacted with other composite systems to, even more rarely, achieve a further advance involving even higher complexity, and so forth.

We do not now know any of the exact steps followed in the incessant, impersonal molecular and molecular system cotillion that constituted pre-social interaction in the pre-life oceans. What we do know is that the result was the development of an elegant, elaborate and uniform biochemistry shared by all present day life. And it would appear that all of this happened before 3.8

billion years ago. The story continues in the next section with the emergence and dominance of the cell.

Cellular Evolution

The first cell-like structures were very likely small, enclosed regions at least semi-protected from the surrounding environment in some fashion. Lipids and/or proteins are ideal candidates because: a) both classes of compound are known to form protective enclaves; and b) both constitute major components of known cell and membrane structures today. Of course, the first, pre-cellular structures may have born little resemblance to modern membranes and cells.

By way of illustration, various experiments in the laboratory have demonstrated the ability for certain molecular mixtures to form enclosures. Lipids have a great propensity to assemble in sheets of molecules and then, under proper circumstances, to fold up in a three-dimensional fashion to create an internal compartment. It thus might be tempting to think that the first pre-cellular enclosures were lipid based.

However, it has also been demonstrated experimentally that solutions of amino acids, the building blocks of proteins, can spontaneously join into long polymers. Then, under the proper conditions and in the presence of other reasonable (believed to have been available) constituents, certain polymers have been shown to condense into microspheres equivalent in size to the lower limits of present day life.

Alternatively, other early base media besides lipid or protein enclosures are possible as well, such as certain clay formations which display remarkable structural and enzymatic functions. Thus, even prior to the appearance of prototype cell-like structures, much simpler systems may have provided important stepping stones. The point is that we don't yet know how cell-like systems first formed or the nature of their prime constituents. But once cells arose, the principle of competitive exclusion (superior beings defeating competitors by more efficiently consuming nutrients that both species need) must have rendered other provincial isolating systems impotent by comparison.

What is so special about a cell? Primary properties that distinguish a cell from non-cellular material include:

- *Genetic Replication* — the cell reproduces through the execution of a wondrous set of carefully orchestrated mechano-chemical steps programmed in nucleic acids (the genetic code) resident in the cell;
- *Isolation* — the internal activities of the cell are carefully protected and segregated from the surrounding environment by an enveloping cell membrane;

- ***Metabolism*** — the cell continuously operates biochemical pathways that tap external energy from sunlight (photosynthesizers) or food (non-photosynthesizers) to constantly sustain the far-from-equilibrium, self-organized state;
- ***Exchange*** — the cell continuously regulates materials that enter and leave the cell through exquisitely specialized processes, collectively termed membrane transport, resident in the cell membrane.

The key characteristics of the typical cell can be found in other collections of matter. But the quintessential fact is that, in the cell, the identified properties are systematically enhanced through meticulously managed and coordinated details of integrated structure and function.

An important sidelight to our story is symbiosis. Symbiosis is defined as an enduring, mutually beneficial relationship between two living organism types, a host and a symbiont. The symbiont is a guest, having adopted the host as a permanent place of residence. The association is valuable to both beings, and the symbiont is therefore clearly to be distinguished from a parasite. The symbiont provides something essential for the survival of the host. In turn, the host proves advantageous to the symbiont as well, perhaps supplying protection, shelter or food.

A spectacular example of a symbiotic relationship is the single-celled *Paramecium bursaria* and a symbiont that resides totally inside the *Paramecium*, an alga *Chlorella*. When viewing a *Paramecium* through the microscope, the most obvious initial features are the thousands of hair-like cilia that line the outer membrane, beating in rhythmic waves, and the golden transparency of the *Paramecium* body. Upon closer inspection, one can discern within the *Paramecium* hundreds of widely dispersed, minute, shiny, green structures, the *Chlorella*. The *Chlorella* are distinct organisms, green plants to be exact, that the *Paramecium* incorporates completely into its cell body but does not metabolize. The *Chlorella* provide the Paramecium with essential ingredients, carbohydrates that the *Chlorella* produce through photosynthesis. In return, The *Paramecium* provides safety for the vulnerable *Chlorella*.

Innumerable other examples could be cited. The point here is that intracellular symbiosis may have provided an innovative means for nature to commandeer new cellular capabilities, as an easier alternative to evolving certain intracellular organelles from scratch.

Along one dimension, there are two types of cells, prokaryotes and eukaryotes. A distinguishing feature relates to the cell nucleus, a membrane enclosed intracellular compartment housing genetic material and other prime operants. The prokaryotes are the more primitive cell form, lacking a cell nucleus.

The penalty apparently has been severe, for the prokaryotes have been relegated solely to the role of single celled organisms throughout the full tenure of earth bound life, even today. The first cellular beings were probably not too different in form compared to modern prokaryotes.

In contrast, the much more complex eukaryotes feature a distinctive cell nucleus. Eukaryotes did not even first appear until about two billion years ago. But once the eukaryotic experiment succeeded, the pace of evolution accelerated and an explosion of complexity ensued.

At first, the era of single celled organisms (exceeding two billion years in duration) meant that every being had to stand alone. But time and relentless experimentation, coupled with the superlative power of self-organization to entrap ever growing complexity in enduring forms, finally produced stunning dividends. Unfolding evolution led to the progressive genesis of cooperative associations where, through division of labor, special skills of individual organisms were combined to provide increased survival value for multiple cell groups. In some cases, such ensembles may have become more and more coherent in their organization, to the point where something akin to multi-cellular organisms emerged.

But even highly organized assemblages of genetically distinct organisms could not ultimately compete with genetically linked beings. An essential ingredient in the emergence of collective cell function was the landmark development of whole-being genetic reproduction. Otherwise, the multi-cellular ensemble of one generation would not have had a reliable means to assure a next generation. A cell aggregate produced by multiple division of an original founding cell would enjoy the situation where all cells shared the same genetic code. For the earliest evolving forms of such replicating cell aggregates, probably any cell of the group could divide and release a founding cell for a new (next generation) cell aggregate. But eventually, as complexity grew through trillions of generations, the cells of aggregates surely began to become specialized, with unique reproductive function ultimately becoming the duty of a particular cell or cellular subgroup of the aggregate. Aggregates of the latter type would have finally achieved the status of a true multi-cellular organism.

The more complicated cells we see around and in us today are conspicuously sophisticated and bristling with purposeful formations. There are a host of intracellular structures, each endowed with marvelously distinct but intricately coupled functions. In addition, the entire interior of the cell is partitioned into myriad compartments by highly ordered membrane boundaries, and the structure and location of individual functions is extraordinarily regular. Several illustrative examples of key components from eukaryotic animal cells are briefly reviewed for perspective:

Nucleus — this is the structural and functional center of the cell; cells that have had their nucleus removed using microsurgery do not live long; the nucleus harbors and manages the genetic code and its readout, activities that dictate most important actions of the entire cell; the nucleus is also the commander of the fascinating chemical and mechanical choreography that constitutes cell replication;

Endoplasmic Reticulum — the ER is a continuous intracellular communications and distribution system that runs throughout the cell; the ER is composed of a system of membranes, folded, refolded and then folded some more to establish an incredible network that compartmentalizes the cell contents into many specialized regions, creating a magnificent division of labor; the metaphor of the cell being a highly organized factory comes strongly to mind;

Ribosomes — the latter entities are particles residing along 'rough' areas of the endoplasmic reticulum; the ribosomes are the seat of protein synthesis, the long protein polymers being assembled by adding each amino acid constituent one at a time; the order of amino acid types is precisely dictated by messenger-RNA molecules that transport coded assembly instructions from the genes in the cell nucleus to the ribosome factory;

Mitochondria — these are independent intracellular organelles in animal cells, composed of an outer membrane and a highly folded system of inner membranes; the mitochondria metabolize sugars and produce energy-rich molecules for use in driving controlled reactions elsewhere;

Ground Substance — found everywhere between the membranes of the endoplasmic reticulum and around the other organelles, the ground substance contains soluble proteins (enzymes of various kinds), RNA (ribonucleic acid), and other soluble components; also present are structures called microtubules and microfilaments, key roles of which are believed to include intracellular mechanics and communications;

Golgi Apparatus — a distinct localized system of membranes that is involved in preparing and packaging proteins for secretion by the cell; and

Cell Membrane — the outer enveloping membrane separating the cell from the surrounding environment; the other membranes of the cell (e.g., endoplasmic reticulum; nuclear membrane; Golgi apparatus) are continuous with the cell membrane, and can be considered to have originally evolved through invaginations of the external cell membrane.

The list could be extended. However, the real issue is that there is striking compartmentalization and extraordinary specialization within typical eukaryotic cells of single celled and multi-cellular organisms.

Such specialization could have arisen strictly through self-organizing processes and natural selection. One intriguing theory describes another route, and there may be degrees of truth in both stories. The symbiotic relationship described earlier for *Paramecium* and *Chlorella* may have happened many times to build some of the observed cellular structures we now see. Eukaryotic cells may have, over time, attracted multiple symbionts, each having quite different characteristics. Initially, the associations probably would have been simply symbiotic, with the host and various symbionts retaining their independence. But, over eons, some of the guests may have progressively lost their own identities, becoming instead a specialized part of the host. Without the ability to survive alone, the incorporated symbionts ceased to exist as separate organisms.

Today's eukaryotic cells, especially those found in the animals and plants of modern earth, feature innumerable layers of specialization. The molecules of life have diversified in detail tremendously. At the level of cellular subsystems, remarkable regularities of reactants and reactions is evident in every conceivable focal zone of the cell. Furthermore, cells amalgamate together in stunning fashion to build tissues, and tissues are combined in fascinating ways to create organs. And the organs are organized in a symbiotic-like manner to form organ systems and ultimately the total organism. Coordination of the parts to realize the whole can be attributed to multiple, elaborate and still incompletely understood systems of communication between various levels of structure and function throughout the organism. The breathtaking order and organization inherent in higher forms of life is humbling to behold.

What Is Life?

We have talked about life at all levels, from pre-living biochemical genesis through cellular and multi-cellular evolution. But life has yet to be defined. The approach was intentional, to provide a solid foundation for developing a definition of what is alive and what is not.

We usually feel capable of recognizing life when we see it, but a simple yet rigorous definition is deceptively difficult. As mentioned earlier, any selected attribute of living organisms can be found in non-living systems as well. Life proves to be an amalgamation of attributes elaborated to unprecedented extremes.

Thus, life must be defined in an operational sense, outlining what living systems do and accomplish. Key elements include but are not limited to the following:

Replication. Typically the first-order property defining life is stipulated to be the ability to reproduce; critically, the process must also pass along information encoding the reproductive actions, so that progeny can again replicate in the same manner (the genetic code is the fundamental basis of reproduction);

Complexity. Living beings exhibit an extent of complexity far greater than non-living systems; furthermore, the complexity is purposeful, having evolved in a fashion to effectively interact in a relevant manner within the ambient environment of the subject system (an attempt to model a higher animal life form in detail, from the sub-cellular to the whole-body level, would be far beyond consideration by modern engineering, even if the brain were ignored);

Order. As discussed in the last chapter, order implies an arrangement of components or steps that is logical or predisposed for efficient function; life epitomizes order at all levels of structure (rendering, as just one example, each human being very nearly identical based on anatomical (macroscopic) and even histological (microscopic) relationships;

Organization. The concept of organization is superficially similar to order, but relates more to function or processes rather than structural arrangement or activity sequencing; living beings exude striking organization on a grand scale (e.g., precisely managing hundreds of tissues and tens of complicated organs and their myriad coordinated interrelationships);

Hierarchies. Biological structure is a breathtaking array characterized by layer upon layer of successive order and organization; emerging properties burst forth everywhere, and the whole reveals vastly more than the sum of its parts (e.g., concentrations of many sub-cellular molecules control elements of cell function which effect nearby and distant cells, tissues, organs and organ systems at great distances, which can effect other nearby and distant cells, tissues, organs, and organ systems, which often induce balance shifts in bodily functions, which induce many individual organ systems, organs, tissues, cells and subcellular processes to adjust, and so on and so on; every layer of the hierarchy, which incidentally could be specified in far, far more detail than this simple example, knows little about what goes on at levels both above and below — virtually every element in this gargantuan system is flying blind);

Feedback. The constellation of subfunctions that constitute living organisms features a broad and intricate network of communications and feedback control systems, providing an elaborate substrate for command and control (hierarchy upon hierarchy of complex positive and negative feedback control systems operate at virtually every one of hundreds of operational layers operating in the typical higher organism — and many of these systems are significantly interlaced);

Coordination. Superb command and control becomes evident when the performance of major subsystems or behavior of the whole organism is observed; the entire organism acts with marvelous coherence and unity (it is astounding, from the vantage point of current human understanding, that this hopelessly complex system works at all, let alone works with incredible accuracy for a lifetime in most individuals);

Adaptability. In spite of a machine-like architecture with intracellular factories and interacting feedback control systems, the future state of an organism is unpredictable; the being continuously adapts to changing internal and external conditions, and even simple life forms solve problems with a measure of chaotic uncertainty (basically, every single-celled or multi-cellular organism is a mix of mechanical structures and chemical processes that directly operate through myriad interconnected chaotic processes that have evolved to play the odds in favor of the host organism — the stunning result is an incredible adaptive ability in an otherwise very machine-like process);

Interdependence. Individual life forms are not independent; organisms invariably must interact with the environment and other forms of life; the details and meaning of life can only truly be fathomed in the context of the entire biosphere of the earth (and maybe beyond, as we shall see); and

Near Perfection. The persistence of life forms depends upon very precise reproduction; however, mistakes (faulty replication) and accidents (genetic changes caused by outside influences, such as radiation or mutagenic agents) occasionally happen; this is quite fortunate, because such errors are the mainstay of evolution and therefore of functional advancement.

There is a huge chasm between the living and non-living. The reason is that the supreme and, especially over eons of time, seemingly inexhaustible self-organizing capabilities of life, vastly superior to non-living systems, rendered life the runaway winner.

Life is sensational in its orderly and purposeful display of behavior. It is hard not to think that living organisms are relentlessly moving toward some goal according to an invisible predetermined plan.

The concept that life is goal-directed is termed teleology. Through history, the mysterious teleological demeanor of biological systems has resulted in countless proposals purporting some kind of underlying development plan. However, attractive and compelling as the teleological view appears, it is fraught with weakness. Close examination reveals not the slightest shred of solid evidence for goal-directed advancement. Furthermore, the evidence and rationale for the alternative extreme, natural evolution driven by chaotic exploration and self-organization, as outlined in the present book, is quite potent, robust and virtually universally accepted today.

How Life Fits into Natural Law

So the working hypothesis for the moment is that life is a self-organizing pattern of activity in otherwise normal matter. Furthermore, the sub-cellular and cellular actions of an organism act mindlessly in response to incident physical forces, with no knowledge of the goal-directed behavior of the whole organism. Yet, somehow, the organism manages to contend with its environment in a coherent and organized fashion and to perpetuate the ancestral chain.

Modern molecular biologists staunchly favor the mechanistic tenets of biology, viewing all phenomena as arising and acting strictly through natural laws. But such consensus is of recent origin. Yet, in their defense, historical biologists were at an extreme disadvantage. For one, the laws of nature were poorly understood. Also, the ability of observations to address something as complex as living material was quite deficient. Finally, people were unaware of the supreme and unexpected potentiality of emerging properties and self-organizing systems.

History has tended to emphasize contrasting extremes. The proponents of goal-directed life, in the limit, professed what has come to be labelled vitalism. Vitalism conveys to the mysterious qualities of living matter some vital essence not possessed by non-living matter. In other words, life was purported to be a separate class of substance, bestowed with behavior at least in part outside the laws of nature. Thus, the belief was that life simply could not be explained by the laws of nature. At the other extreme from vitalism was the doctrine of reductionism. The limit of reductionism stipulates that, once all basic physical processes operating in a living organism are known, life will have been totally explained. In other words, life is nothing but the underlying mechanisms of normal physics.

The vast majority of modern scientists disavow the emotional rigidity and unsubstantiated assumptions and claims of both the vitalist and reductionist extremes. The tenets of the contemporary accord have been termed mechanism. The mechanistic theory of life contends that living things are complex machines that operate through the normal laws of physics and under the action of normal physical forces. The distinction between the living and non-living is due to different degrees of complexity, and nothing more. All the properties of life are inherent in the constituent biochemical molecules and therefore, one more step removed, normal atoms.

But doesn't this just sound like a disguised version of reductionism? In a word, no. The difference between reductionism and mechanism is that the reductionists ignore emerging properties and the stunning consequences that make the real world come alive. The mechanist agrees that the underpinnings reside in usual laws acting through normal forces. But the mechanist goes far beyond the latter limit to also look at the fascinating animated self-organization that is the ultimate origin, salvation and expression of living material. This may help explain why the present story has devoted the last three chapters to relentlessly discussing emerging properties and self-organization. A deep appreciation of the latter phenomena, at every level, is truly necessary to properly appreciate the tremendous insight and strength of the mechanistic approach. Biology will never be properly reconciled with physics until we come to grips with the fact that emerging properties and hierarchically evolving self-organization magically bring into existence new and unfathomed processes that are simply meaningless at lower levels of complexity.

One of the strongest arguments for a purpose to life and the universe is the provocative unfolding of totally new phenomena as one ascends the hierarchy of complexity. The latter is true both within an individual organism and especially in looking at an overview of life. This will become more apparent as the story proceeds.

Life Beyond Earth

Current evidence suggests the high likelihood of other life in the universe. However, the catch is the phrase 'current evidence.' We have not succeeded in observing life directly anywhere external to the earth, nor have we detected any signals from the solar system or deep space even slightly suggestive of life elsewhere. All current evidence is indirect.

First, it is important to specify a critical ground rule. The present discussion will be limited to the consideration of life forms similar to that on earth, at least in terms of dependence on organic molecules in roughly the terrestrial range of temperatures. Other forms of life beyond such organic life may very well exist. However, for present purposes, it is only necessary to consider life with a fundamental nature similar to the earth bound variety. This is not necessarily very limiting. Carbon, the basis of organic molecules and therefore terrestrial life, is an atom that, above all others, excels in forming bonds with other atoms. In turn, water is the most abundant molecule in the universe likely to exist in the liquid state. Thus, perhaps we shouldn't be surprised to find ourselves immersed in and composed of organic molecules in solutions of water.

A concise perspective on earth life is pertinent. We live within a nominal spiral galaxy, the 10 billion year old Milky Way, about two-thirds of the distance toward the end of one spiral arm and somewhat beside it. Earth orbits the sun, a typical star that exists midway through a process termed the main sequence (the hydrogen burning phase of star life). The details are not important, but most stars reside on the main sequence for a significant portion of their existence. Main sequence stars are believed to be reasonably stable in terms of temperature and radiation, and stars near the size of the sun are expected to show such stability for about 10 billion years. The sun formed through condensation of local galactic gas and dust about five billion years ago, and the earth formed soon thereafter. On the earth, less than a billion years were required for single celled life to evolve, and nearly another four billion years passed prior to the appearance of highly intelligent life.

Earth's home, the Milky Way galaxy, contains on the order of 100 billion stars. Within the Milky Way, stars with planets are believed common (a number have been recently discovered nearby), and there are probably millions and possibly billions of planets similar to earth in temperature and general chemical makeup. Furthermore, there are billions of other galaxies similar to the Milky Way in the observable universe.

Life may be improbable. But given hundreds of millions of years under reasonable conditions in a suitable environment, available evidence exists, some controversial, that life based on organic molecules is not only possible but appears probable. Furthermore, a large number of organic molecules, some quite complicated, have been found to exist in enormous clouds of gas and dust pervading the Milky Way. A few workers have suggested that planets might get seeded by such space-borne organics, circumventing the need for biochemical evolution to create life from scratch. However, whether seeding occurs is not important to the present argument. The point is that organic molecules identical to many of those believed important to the birth of life on earth exhibit a potent propensity to form from simpler raw materials, even under the often brutal conditions of interstellar space.

The age of the universe is 15 billion years. Some time elapsed before galaxies formed, and, in any case, the Milky Way did not arise until 5 billion years later. In addition, once the Milky Way formed, several generations of rapidly evolving stars were required to successively appear and die, to build up the a more modern complement of chemical elements in galactic gas and dust clouds. The reason is that young galaxies are almost entirely made up of the few lightest elements (principally hydrogen and helium). Heavier elements, including carbon, oxygen, nitrogen and many others, are literally manufactured through nuclear fusion reactions in certain star cores, and then dispersed into space when the stars die. Since the solar system contains significant quantities of the heavier elements, several generations of relatively rapidly developing Milky Way stars must have preceded the cloud of dust and gas from which the solar system is believed to have coalesced.

As the young Milky Way matured over several billion years, countless earth-like planets must have formed throughout the galaxy. Our solar system is only on the order of 4.5 billion years old, only a fraction of the galactic age.

Thus, hoards of planets sporting life, some portion with intelligent life, may have arisen far in advance of life on earth. On the other hand, the rise of such loci of intelligence would be expected to be staggered in time on a geological scale. Humanity has only begun, from the perspective of solid science, to contemplate our place in the universe in very recent times, say this century. Therefore, at the moment, we probably represent the youngest intelligence in the Milky Way.

The discovery of life elsewhere in the universe would have profound impact on humanity. Perspective on our suspected place in the universe would be, once and for all, relegated to actual fact instead of academic musings. However, distances are far too great for near-term direct sampling of other worlds. As an alternative, active earth bound searches are now underway in an attempt to detect signals from deep space conveying signs of thoughtful origin, the idea being to detect other intelligent life by virtue of its technology.

Conclusion to Part I

To review, then, the major highlights of Part I, we have come to portray matter as an astonishing, robust, prolific, self-organizing material that seems quite resourceful and brilliant in action. Matter is purposeful in result but does not in any way follow a preordained plan. The purposefulness arises automatically from the relentless testing of new accidental renditions against old models relative to virtually every cosmic constituent, or in other words, from natural selection. Providing the fodder for natural selection, new complexities of matter arise by virtue of random exploration of form and substance through chaotic actions, novel forms becoming locked into permanence if there is on hand the proper conditions and an ongoing energy supply to sustain the added complexity. This provides, within the context of the present interpretation, the short answer to Central Question [1] identified in Chapter One, "How Does Matter Come to Create organized Structure?" A more detailed answer, integrated with responses to the other five Central Questions of Chapter One, are presented near the end of Chapter Ten (at the end of Part III).

The pinnacle of self-organized matter on earth is the human brain. As mentioned previously, the human brain is in fact the most complex system in the known universe, exceeding by far all forms of non-living matter. At the top of normal brain function sits consciousness, the mysterious something that makes us who we are. As the present book unfolds, the function of consciousness and its role in the universe will become a main theme. And to the latter end, it is time to turn attention to Part II of the book, where we delve deeply into the elusive tapestry of mind and consciousness.

PART II

Brain, Mind, and Consciousness

PART II

Brain, Mind, and Consciousness

Part I addressed matter, its stunning propensity to self-organize, and introduced the highest expression of self-organization, life. Part II will now focus on the brain and mind in general, and in particular of animals and especially humans. Consciousness will also be a main topic of discourse. At some time during the early rise of animals on earth, the phenomenon of vague awareness arose from a robotic substrate. The new primordial tool must have born adaptive advantage, and progressively prospered to create the advanced consciousness, the portion of our mind (total mental activity) of which we are constantly aware, that humans experience today.

But what is this thing we call consciousness (closely akin to the concept of intelligence). Consciousness is that portion of the mind that manifests our immediate experience. Consciousness is not a thing but a process, designed to permit ongoing analysis and intentional adaptation of responses in light of a broader perspective or context than that permitted by automatic behavior. As an analogy, bombs in general follow a ballistic course, their path being fully determined (ignoring air resistance and wind) once flight is initiated. But the trajectory of smart bombs can be altered after launch, providing for mid-course corrections and improved performance. Consciousness, the spotlight of focused attention and ongoing experience, is the supreme attribute of life and the penultimate accomplishment of earthbound self-organization. In fact, humans have carried consciousness to startling new heights, embodying the invention of the next level of conscious complexity, a new phenomenon we will term self-consciousness.

We will see that the brain is in the business of processing data, and is, to the dismay and disbelief of many, in essence a computer. Even though we feel a powerful self-identity and a unity of mind, we will see that, in fact, the brain is really a collection of relatively independent, stand-alone processors with their own selfish desires and motives. Finally, we will argue that the results of brain function and the phenomenon of mind are really one and the same, distinct aspects of the same events viewed on different planes of abstraction (there is no soul).

Part II's provocative look at mind, along with Part I's fresh view of matter, are crucial to fully develop and interpret ideas about god, the cosmos and our existence featured in Part III.

Chapter 5

The Mysteries of Consciousness

The Temporal Flow of Perceptions

Consciousness is the supreme attribute of life. Hardly anyone would dispute such an assertion. In consciousness we find our real identity, and feel that our superior level of consciousness clearly distinguishes humans from other animals. But trying to define the elusive consciousness is a lot like attempting to quantify life — we sense that we know life and consciousness when we see them, but capturing their mysterious essence is a daunting and perplexing problem.

One elementary proposition depicts consciousness as the temporal flow of perceptions. This simple and tangible description will serve temporarily to begin discussion, but will be modified later. To frame the concept in a familiar metaphor, consciousness is like a movie. Individual snapshots of our momentary world focus are presented rapidly enough so that the individual frames merge seamlessly into a regular, continuous whole.

Care must be taken, however, not to push the metaphor too far. Exact adherence to a movie frame model implies a digital-like process where true, distinct frames (mental images) are actually processed as units. In contrast, the other extreme is an analog-like approach, where data is monitored and processed continuously and is endlessly blended into a smooth, coherent experience. We don't yet know if the mechanism of consciousness is most like a digital, analog, or some digital-analog hybrid process.

An important point is to distinguish between individual movie frames and the interrelationship between frames. As we shall see, consciousness is not felt to result from perceptions and interpretations involved in a single frame. Rather, at least in part, consciousness seems related to the relationship between the current frame and frames from the immediate past. Consciousness is, above all, the dynamics of subjective experience, not a succession of static views. In other words, consciousness appears to derive more from the interpretive connection between moments, not the moments themselves.

One more introductory concept is critical. The term consciousness has not been uniformly applied in the popular and scientific literature. Nevertheless, a precise definition is essential to the present dialog. To reiterate the explanation presented in Chapter One, consciousness will be used here to denote the state of ongoing awareness, thought, emotion and volition characteristic of advanced, independent control. Dynamic, ongoing, flowing experience of one's body and the world around, in the context of the self and of past experience, is taken to make up 'normal' consciousness.

The use of the word 'normal' in the latter statement must be qualified. Actually, consciousness is not a singular state or process. We can easily recognize different levels or altered states of consciousness in humans, such as sleep, dreaming, relaxation, fully awake, heightened arousal, inebriation, etc.). Similar states of consciousness are ascribed to the higher animals. Also, consciousness appears to be a property possessed by different species as a matter of degree, rather than an all-or-nothing property. Most people would concur that the typical level of consciousness generally declines through the following series: humans; dogs; sheep; rats; trout; insects; and rocks. Average consciousness also varies at different times during a being's lifetime.

Mind, Brain and Consciousness

To borrow another definition from Chapter One, we adopt the view that to label something as a mind is to say that it has the capacity to think. In broader terms, mind is the thing that: a) senses and perceives external events; b) internally feels, remembers, recalls, and imagines, based on internal stores and external happenings; c) through attention, monitors and manages 'interesting' (not-subconscious) eventualities; and d) wills and instigates actions on elements of the outside world.

Where is the mind located? Mind is the mental activity of the brain, and nothing more. This position is the strong consensus of brain and cognitive scientists, although a few dissenters exist. In other words, in the vast mainstream view, mind is the total aggregate of all brain-driven mental activity occurring at any time. Consciousness, on the other hand, is much more restrictive. Consciousness is our flowing or sweeping window of comprehension, composed of our immediate continuous experience of the world around us. Consciousness is certainly an ongoing mental event, and therefore is part of the mind. However, as will be shown, we do not appreciate multitudes of subconscious mental actions that occur in parallel with consciousness, but all such activities are generally included within the realm of mind.

So, consciousness (conscious awareness) must be distinguished from subconscious awareness. Subconscious awareness means active cognitive detection of information about the bodily or environmental status of the subject being, or about the organism's past experiences, that is outside the realm of immediate awareness.

The distinction between conscious and subconscious awareness has a sound neurophysiological basis. The seat of subconscious awareness appears to be the reticular activating system of the brain stem, a primitive part of the lowest major structural level in the human brain forming a major enlargement at the top of the spinal cord (see Fig. 5.1 below). Activities in the brain stem's reticular activating system are believed to be largely if not entirely subconscious. In contrast, the seat of consciousness is believed to reside basically in the cerebral cortex, a thin, enveloping sheet of layered cells that forms the surface of the brain (some very recent evidence also implicates the thalamus, a deep brain structure), and is generally considered to represent the highest level of brain function. Put another way, subconscious awareness needs only sensory data, and does not require even a modicum of perception (sensation interpreted in the light of experience). Consciousness, in turn, not only depends on perception, but also intelligence (the ability to think).

Let's then take the opportunity to summarize key relationships developed so far. An analogy with a computer may be instructive. The analogy is intentionally loose, however, and is not intended to imply whether or not the brain functions like a computer (that is a topic for later discussion). The brain is the physical system (the hardware) within which the mind (the software) operates. Consciousness appears only when the software is running. Crudely, consciousness might be considered somewhat analogous to the information that appears moment by moment on the computer screen, but does not reflect the background processing by the computer software for producing the screen display or any other background activities, hardware or software, unrelated to screen presentation.

The Incredible Structure of the Brain

At first glance, the brain exterior is a monochrome mass conveying little intrigue. But once we delve inside, awesome, intricate structure and tremendous organization come alive through conspicuous albeit bewildering detail.

Figure 5.1 depicts key views of the intact human brain. At the lowest level of description, three structures can be identified: a) the large overlying cerebrum, the cerebellum in the lower rear aspect, and the brain stem, on which the cerebellum sits and over the top of which the cerebrum wraps. The brain is an extraordinary extension and elaboration of the spinal cord. Note that the cerebrum is also divided down the middle, front to back, into the right and left cerebral hemispheres. In turn, each hemisphere is segregated into four portions, respectively designated the frontal, parietal, temporal, and occipital lobes.

There is an incredible and fascinating amount of information known about the interior structure of the brain. However, such detail is beyond the scope of the present treatment. For current purposes, several fundamental aspects of functional brain organization are concisely reviewed below.

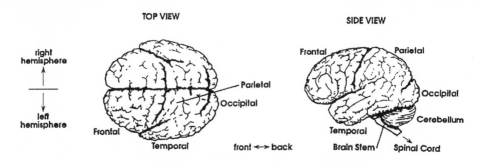

Figure 5.1 Major structures of the human brain*

The Top View indicates division of the cerebrum into right and left hemispheres, and also defines the four cerebral lobes of each hemisphere (Frontal; Parietal; Temporal; Occipital). The Side View depicts three prominent structures, the brain stem (a substantially expanded extension of the spinal cord), the cerebellum (attached to the brain stem), and the cerebrum (not labeled) with its four principal lobes.

* Adapted from Fig. 9.1, *The Emperor's New Mind* by Roger Penrose, 1991, Penguin Books, with permission.

Both the cerebellum and the cerebrum are proportionately larger in humans, relative to the rest of the brain, than is true for other animals. But it is especially the cerebrum that is decreed to be humankind's highest attribute. The outer layer of both the cerebrum and cerebellum are covered with a thin surface layer of gray matter termed, respectively, the cerebral cortex and the cerebella cortex. Underlying the gray matter in both structures is a thicker layer of white matter. The gray matter represents substantial areas of brain cells, highlighted by neurons, the cells that carry out various types of neural processing. In turn, the white matter is predominantly formed from long nerve fibers that interconnect the neurons in various subsystems of diverse brain structures.

For brevity, discussion will first center on the three most prominent (in humans) sensory systems, the tactile (somatosensory), visual and auditory. For each respective sense, an important fraction of incoming sensory information travels to a special area termed the primary sensory cortex of the cerebrum. The primary sensory cortex for each sense has a distinctive location (Figure 5.2). The primary sensory systems represent prominent (but certainly not the only) inputs to the cerebrum for each sensory system. In turn, a particularly pronounced portion of brain output is found to originate in one area called the primary motor cortex.

The primary areas of the cortex, both sensory and motor, closely communicate with adjacent cortical sectors termed secondary areas, which in turn are adjacent to tertiary (also termed association) areas. Thus, for example, the primary visual cortex is surrounded on several sides by secondary visual cortex, which is in turn surrounded by tertiary visual cortex. The same conceptual

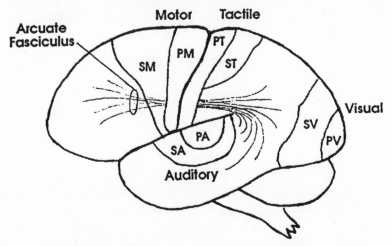

Figure 5.2 First-order functional relationships of the human cerebrum*

The general locations of four functional systems of the cerebral cortex are indicated, each comprised of a Primary (P) and Secondary (S) zone: Motor Cortex (PM Primary; SM Secondary); Tactile (PT Primary; ST Secondary), more formally termed the Somatosensory Cortex; Auditory (PA Primary; SA Secondary); and Visual (PV Primary; SV Secondary). Also shown schematically is the Arcuate Fasciculus, a very prominent neural pathway that courses front-to-back through each hemisphere, left and right (see Fig. 5.1 for definition of hemispheres). Cortical areas lying between the four labeled regions are termed Tertiary or Association Cortex, and relate to higher level integrated processing.

* Adapted from Fig, 9.5, *The Emperor's New Mind* by Roger Penrose, 1991, Penguin Books, with permission.

arrangement is also true for the auditory and tactile sensory systems. The tertiary sectors blend together and become indistinguishable in regions located between the three main sensory areas.

Notice from Figure 5.2 that the motor system basically occupies the frontal portion of the brain, in a front-to-back sense, while the three sensory systems are deployed to the middle and rear. In a very simplistic view, the cerebrum works as follows. Incoming sensory data first enters the appropriate primary sensory area, and then spreads outward to the secondary areas for intermediate analysis and finally to the tertiary (association) areas as the data becomes more completely comprehended. Brain output follows a conceptually reverse path. Initial glimmers of an output arise in the tertiary motor area, are elaborated further in the secondary motor sector, and reach final definition in the primary motor output area. There is a very prominent nerve pathway (actually, one for each of the left and right cerebral hemispheres), termed the arcuate fasciculus, that connects the middle and rear portions of the cerebrum (among other functions, dedicated to sensory processing) with the frontal lobe (accompanying other activities, devoted to motor processing). In our greatly simplified model, then, the somewhat intermingled tertiary sensory regions talk to each other and arrive at some consensus, which is then passed to the motor system by way of the arcuate fasciculus for the formulation of motor output.

It is essential to point out that the picture above is vastly oversimplified. There are innumerable other areas of the brain that become involved at all levels of sensory, associative and motor processing. Furthermore, the primary sensory and motor areas do far more than depicted above. The purpose here is merely to form a modest framework as background for later discussion.

Is Consciousness Necessary?

All but the simplest animal species possess some form of nervous system. The most primitive nervous systems typically form one or more reflex arcs, a pathway composed of one or more nerve cells arranged in series. A reflex arc begins where some form of internal or outside influence is detected, and the arc conveys a representation of said influence (coded in nerve cell activity) to some source of action (a muscle or gland; an effector).

Really primitive nervous systems may merely possess one or more reflex arcs that behave essentially independently. But as the ladder of nervous system complexity is ascended, by focusing on higher and higher species, without exception, once even a barely discernible complexity is manifest, one area (usually at what would be termed the functional front end of the organism) becomes more prominent and assumes a role of higher level processing for integrating the activity in multiple pathways. The reason is that even primitive behaviors, such as reflexes, function more effectively if the reflex pathway from sensation to movement passes through some level of central processing. This allows the opportunity for other pathways to exert influence on the subject pathway prior to any induced response, a tremendous adaptive advantage.

For illustration, the brain and the spinal cord make up the human central nervous system. The human withdrawal reflex from, say, touching hot pavement with a bare foot, passes through the spinal cord. By relaying through a portion of the central nervous system, the withdrawal reflex provides an opportunity for other pathways to influence the action. As a case in point, if both of our feet suddenly impinge on hot pavement, hardly any of us would lift both legs at the same time. We have learned that, due to relentless gravity, the immediate consequences would be worse yet (we could quickly find our posterior torso abruptly meeting the ground with, minimally, a painful thud). Instead, there is a brain-based override of the otherwise potent withdrawal reflex, usually inducing in this case a wise alternative strategy to rapidly quick step in a direction that portends relief. Interestingly, the decision and initial acts for the alternative behavior are subconscious, and only later does the person consciously reflect on the events (we will have much more to say about this startling point below).

So, even subconscious mind can serve us well. But what is the use of consciousness? Of course, we would all complain loudly if our precious consciousness were turned off, because that is really what creates our real self, our identity. But it is important to take an evolutionary rather than a parochial perspective. Why did not animals forever rely on reflexes and other automatic behaviors to respond to the environment? Given sufficient sophistication, it would seem quite possible for exquisitely elaborate response capabilities to be completely automated. In fact, our subconscious mind is a marvelous example of just such a system (as developed below). So who needs consciousness?

As a first principle, life is basically an adaptive process. Automated response systems can function in a reasonable manner only to the extent that the eliciting situations are repeatable. Variations in the situation context or detail can rather easily render a simple reflex inappropriate, as we saw in the hot pavement example above. As a second principle, systems that have evolved the ability to contemplate situation context and detail in advance, and/or to better interpret ramifications of the present situation, and adapt responses appropriately, would likely realize superior performance in the long run. Within the brutal and impersonal world in the wild, a meaningful improvement in survivability would expectedly accrue, on average, in proportion to a being's repertoire of adaptive skills.

The epitome of adaptation is consciousness. The individual being that can think is better able to offset other disadvantages of raw capability or unforeseen circumstances, and on the average, is more likely to survive and reproduce. Thus, it is likely that animal evolution conveyed meaningful benefits to the origin of consciousness in primitive species. Further, given the appearance of consciousness in some primal form, the expansion and elaboration of the phenomenon would be, statistically, even more beneficial. Thus, the favorable evolutionary pressures would render progressive enhancement of the phenomenon virtually inevitable.

General Properties of the Mind

Adaptation involves choosing the best available alternative, not the best of all possible choices. The mind is viewed as attending to the immediate situation, and comparing the options that consciously or subconsciously appear (come to mind).

At different times, the same situation may generate different alternatives for consideration, depending on prior situational context or mental state. Your decision of how to get to a nearby appointment (whether to walk, drive, ride a bike, take a cab or bus, etc.), and the route to be followed, can vary dramatically depending on the time, mental state, schedule, neighborhood safety, memory of past occurrences, and a host of other variables. Thus, the mind is driven by the immediate environment and current priorities, in the context of previous experience. Surprisingly, we don't have to be perfect or to have superior knowledge. Rather, we bend with the wind, doing the best that we can. But, over time, the accrued benefits of even modest adaptive abilities collectively breed significant advantages.

Immediacy of Mind. Throughout evolution, the needs of organisms have been basically immediate in nature. Long-range planning is not and apparently has never been a major requirement for animals in the wild. For this reason, the mind evolved to record, interpret and react to changes in the environment right away. In computer jargon, the mind developed to operate in real time.

So dynamic happenings are the stuff that drives the nervous system, whereas unchanging realms are largely ignored. When we are first learning a new task, the mind is attentive to detail and deliberate in action. However, as the task or situation becomes more familiar, the mind relegates what was the main focus of consciousness to a progressively more subconscious role. When we are initially learning to drive, it is a daunting ordeal to struggle through all of the important considerations and actions. But later, once driving has become routine, we may not remember much detail after navigating our car completely across town. This is in spite of the fact that we likely had to contend with innumerable traffic lights, pedestrians, competing vehicles and numerous other challenges.

The importance of adaptation can be expected to rise in proportion to the complexity of the environment. Hardly any higher being experiences the exact situation twice. Differences, from subtle to stark, creep in even when we contrive to keep parameters fixed. Therefore, of necessity, the mind developed to respond to gradients or differences, rather than absolutes. The same abrupt utterance may evoke startle in a quiet room, but hardly a discernible reaction in a noisy stadium.

It is critical that we try to understand the mind in the context of evolution. Evolution of land animals has proceeded for hundreds of millions of years, and that of modern humans for tens of thousands of years. Yet humans have only possessed written language for several thousand years, and we have only begun to legitimately understand ourselves during the present century. The brain and its emergent mind evolved to get by in the wild, not in modern cultures of the industrial world. And there has been far too little time since the socialization of man for the brain to undergo drastic alteration of ingrained age-old strategies.

Individuality of Minds. Another key attribute is that minds are individual. Everyone is different, even identical twins. Identical twins have exactly the same genetic makeup, but not identical histories.

At birth, the mind has spectacular potential, but also exhibits tremendous latitude in terms of ultimate elaboration and expression. Because of the way that the brain develops, the world becomes different to each of us. Everyone comes into the world in a distinct situation. We are thrust into a unique family (or lack thereof) and environment, and the complex interplay between all relevant elements creates the foundation for incredible diversity. Additionally, we are exposed to an endless succession of novel moments throughout life. No other person, even given an identical genetic makeup and living in the same environment, would feel the same feelings and make a lifetime of decisions in exactly the same way as you.

Wiring The Brain. The brain contains on the order of 10 billion neurons (brain cells). Each neuron, on average, makes an estimated ten thousand connections to other neurons. Due to the highly convoluted form of the brain surface, the thin, outermost, sheet-like cerebral cortex makes up a surprising one-fourth of total brain volume. But even more astonishing is the fact that the cortex contains about three-fourths of all brain neurons. It is not even remotely possible that the genetic code could specify the hopeless task of precisely wiring the brain, because far too much data would be required. So how does nature accomplish this seemingly impossible task?

Brain development serves as yet another demonstration of the colossal power of self-organization, that is, of evolutionary experimentation coupled with natural selection and eons of time. The following scenario, greatly simplified to aid understanding, unfolds while the fetus is in the womb.

Early in development, both within and between defined brain centers that ultimately have basic functional relationships, the brain largely wires everything to everything else non-selectively. But the vast majority of such neuron connections prove useless. The reason is that most first-round connections fail to logically relate to emerging nervous system inputs from outside the developing brain (the fetal body or womb environment) or in a functional fashion with other neurons in the brain. The developing brain also incessantly sends throughout its numerous centers a broad based barrage of internally-generated signals. These signals are directed along, in terms of ultimate brain organization, initially imprecise pathways but that loosely relate to ordered functional relationships in a mature brain. Over time, the vast majority of first-round neuronal connections prove to be meaningless or of low value (they do not logically fit into one or more functional systems, and so they do not regularly respond to ambient activity in a systematic fashion). Such connections that are not regularly 'exercised' atrophy and disappear.

Thus, the developing brain greatly over-connects at first, but then drastically prunes, through a process termed neuronal selection, all but the few pathways that prove to be meaningful based on functional interrelationships.

Pre-programming. The old adage of the mind at birth being a blank slate has merit, but is too extreme. At a very general level, gross brain interrelationships are determined genetically. But as we have seen, even in the womb, some influences from within the brain and fetus and from the fetal surroundings begin to uniquely shape the developing mind as well. Later, environmentally based neural selection becomes especially prominent after birth, being of monumental importance in early development. The process also continues in a more subdued mode throughout life.

Under genetic pre-programming, gross brain structure and brain center interrelationships are defined in a very general way from inception forward, independent of environmental influences. Thus the slate is not even blank at the human blueprint level. Much gross structure, such as the crude interconnections between different general brain centers or areas, is pre-defined. In contrast, a substantial portion of the fine structure of connections within many brain centers is pruned and set by brain-derived test signals, internal activity of the organism in general, and influences from the environment.

A pointed example of genetic pre-programming is the innate fear of many primates and some humans to snakes, snake-like movement, or the silhouette of a snake, even if no prior knowledge of snakes is present. Receptivity for language may also be preordained in humans. On the other hand, acquiring a specific language, various practiced hand-eye coordination skills, and manual dexterity are examples of learned elements that profoundly effect the fine structure connectivity and relative strength of neuron-to-neuron connections in broad areas of the brain.

Multiple Minds. We are a collection of minds. Enshroud the eyes of a young animal during a critical period of early development, and profound, permanent disruption of vision ensues. But it isn't just the major senses that act as minds. Some of the potential pathways that become eliminated through developmental disuse are parts of possible minds for other individuals raised under different circumstances. Especially during the long period of human infancy, the early environment selects and grooms the specific minds that survive. What we end up with as adults is a somewhat disjointed collection of senses and individual skills (which we shall call mindlets, a concept developed in Chapter 2) that act remarkably independently. Due to the enormous number of contributing parameters and therefore the incalculable probabilities of random duplication, we are all unique individuals.

The concept of multiple minds (a collection of mindlets) is not just a descriptive convenience. The brain did not originally evolve to think. Most of ancient brain development occurred to enhance control of various body reactions. Those activities revered as most human, such as language, perception and intelligence, represent only a small portion of brain function.

The cerebral cortex is commonly labeled, for brevity, as the cortex. It is believed to be the supreme level of brain processing, and displays a telling organization. The cortex forms the outer surface of nearly the entire cerebrum, and is a sheet-like structure composed of several distinct layers with a total thickness of only about one-eighth inch. The cortex is arranged as an extensive side-by-side array of cylindrical columns of cells. Each column extends all the way from the lower to the upper sheet-like surface of the cortex, and therefore penetrates all cortical layers. The columns are specialized functionally. For example, some columns in the visual lobe of the cortex detect and process data on corners, edges or movements of objects in the visual field of view. In other words, each column is a data processing module for extracting and processing highly selected aspects of information.

Brain function happens through a sequence of hierarchical layers of processing at successively higher levels of abstraction. Corners or edges (tangible geometrical elements) may be the business of a cortical module in the primary visual area. However, for a module in the visual tertiary area, object identification may be the task, using not only collective geometrical data, but information on size, color, movement, location and surroundings, past history, and so forth. We take it for granted, but the brain is wondrous in its analytical flexibility. We are able not only to recognize, say, a table lamp, but we also can picture the object in our mind without visual input and even rotate and scale the image at will. This is an awesome capability that we routinely conduct without training.

Assemblages of columnar cortical modules make up what will be termed skill units. Our composite skills such as walking, speaking, writing, brushing our teeth, and countless other examples, are made up of a complex, coordinated array of individual skill units. Our composite skills, or just skills for short, exist as entities at several levels of description, including mental, behavioral, physiological and anatomical. If each skill unit is imagined as a tiny patch, the cortex becomes a strikingly convoluted patchwork quilt. Skill units have a close correlation to the agents and agencies of Minsky, discussed in the model of the mind developed near the end of Chapter 2.

So, mind is an intricate and ever changing product of genetics and environment, of nature and nurture. The human brain even before birth enters the scene with a huge oversupply of nerve circuits and connections. Then, the connections and circuits are pruned and tuned through relentless neural selection, both before and after birth. Evolution does not result in a system that enables every organism to perfectly adapt. Rather, beings evolve to endow the average representative of the subject species with the average number and level of abilities for the average environment encountered. The operating watchword is indirectly the survival of the individual, but far more importantly, the statistical survival of the species.

Each individual has an extensive repertoire of skills. Most skills are well practiced, and ingrained skills have been found to be, under normal circumstances, largely if not entirely unconscious. Consciousness decides when to stroke a putt, and may even focus on one aspect of the putting act (a particular skill) in an attempt to improve performance. Even so, we are generally unaware of the vast majority of skill units making up the gross activity. Each skill represents, in effect, an independent mindlet governing many sub-elements, and the unique complement of mindlets that we each possess as a total organism is exclusively determined through neuronal selection acting on the given genetic substrate.

Independence of Minds. Our many mindlets behave, in great part, independently. But normally, as we will see below, only one high-level mindlet is in control.

A spectacular contrast can be seen in the human split-brain preparation. Developed originally to treat certain severe cases of epilepsy, the procedure involves surgically cutting the corpus callosum. The corpus callosum is a huge neural pathway (composed of 200 million axons, or long neuron output processes) that connects the right and left halves of the brain (the right and left cerebral hemispheres; see Fig. 5.1). Under unchallenging circumstances, a naïve observer would be hard pressed to notice anything wrong with a split brain subject. On closer scrutiny, however, a startling result can be demonstrated. Split brain people exhibit at any one moment the existence of two independent controlling minds, one residing in each cerebral hemisphere.

But the real focus of the present discussion is, again, normal people with intact brains. Normal individuals feature different centers of mind (higher-level mindlets), each competing for center stage. We will say that only one high-level mindlet is in control at any one time, because that is what we experience. Furthermore, the transitions from one governing mindlet to another, as we suddenly shift from one activity to something else, for instance, are remarkably smooth and continuous. Therefore, close observation is required to reveal our multiple personalities. In addition, multiple mindlets not being bad enough, we often don't know what we are doing until we observe what we have already done. How many times have you been in a situation where you would like to tell someone off, but know better. Yet, at some point, you may let fly anyway, without forethought, and then ask yourself how did that happen? Your competing angry mindlet, which had been subdued for awhile, finally broke through. And the act had already occurred (or at least had begun) before another more subdued mindlet could intercede.

Thus, we are really a collection of mindlets, with one mindlet constantly in provisional control. Command can be rapidly passed to one of the other mindlets, depending on eventualities. The transition is so smooth that we don't usually recognize the switch of control. In fact, remarkably, we think 'we' are in charge at all times. However, the competing mindlets also have competing interests, so, in fact, 'we' are not one unified personality. Additionally, the majority of mindlet actions are subconscious, and so, mostly, we really don't know what 'we' are doing.

The Unsettling Delays of Consciousness

It feels like we are in control of our actions. However, recent evidence reveals some shocking facts. It appears that many if not all of our movements are planned and initiated outside of consciousness, by one or another of our subconscious mindlets.

Distinctive brain wave patterns have been detected that signal the preparation for movement. Termed the readiness potential, this represents a characteristic brain wave signature occurring from one-half to three seconds before voluntary action. Importantly, the readiness potential does not precede reflex action, just volitional moves. Processes accompanying the interval of the readiness potential include prediction of what part of the body will be moved, not just some kind of housekeeping. So the brain is preparing to move even before we become aware of an 'intentional' movement. Yet we do not perceive a delay between command and execution. This is truly a startling result. Are we in charge at all? Are automatic, unconscious processes really directing the system, with consciousness providing an illusion of 'our' control?

The answer is yes, at least in part. The existence of independent centers of neural control in the mind have been demonstrated experimentally. The result is a clawing maelstrom of individual mindlets grasping for control. Conflict is a fundamental element of mind play. A 'volitional' act therefore begins before we become aware that we have decided to act. Sometimes we can cancel the action, once we become aware, but other times it is already too late. The subconscious is not one large unseen army, but an array of at least semi-independent unconscious mindlets, each with its own agenda. We are at least similar to a multiple personality, organized and controlled to some extent by consciousness.

But the dissociation of consciousness from reality is even worse. We have the impression that, at least, we finally see the action as it actually unfolds. Sorry, but that doesn't really seem to be true either. It has been shown that other brain centers are aware of what is happening before consciousness.

It appears that consciousness constructs experience in the following manner. A sense organ records an event, and distributes signals to various brain systems. One such pathway takes the signal very rapidly (within milliseconds) to the primary sensory area of the cerebral cortex that deals with the relevant sensation. However, awareness of the stimulus only reaches consciousness after a delay of one-half second or so, and even then, only if the sensation is deemed important enough to break into conscious experience. Yet we experience the event at the time of the original signal arrival at the cortex. The brain apparently adjusts the time axis of awareness to eliminate the delay incurred in the subconscious processing employed to decide whether to alert conscious experience. So even though we may eventually know about the event, our knowledge is: a) delayed in time; b) altered so that we don't know that it's delayed in time; and c) therefore, a period exists where all responses of a rapid nature are solely subconscious, consciousness entering the scene only later, if at all.

The Inseparable Role of Memory

Memories are the most enduring characteristic that we possess. The elderly can remember items spanning a lifetime. A comment by another can trigger a spontaneous appearance of images or detail thought to be forgotten long ago. Memory defines who we are and shapes our actions more than any other personal dimension.

Our thoughts and actions are largely determined by ideas, memories and drives that are unconscious and even inaccessible to consciousness. Much of the latter statement follows from the previous discussion of our many mindlets. However, there is an added element, that of memory. Consciousness and memory are in a certain sense inseparable, there being no memory without an accompanying conscious state. Furthermore, as we shall see in the next chapter, memory provides an essential component of consciousness. Thus, a complete understanding of consciousness (which science has not achieved as yet) will undoubtedly require a thorough understanding of memory (which also has not as yet been accomplished).

Consciousness is a state of awareness. Most animals probably experience awareness to some degree, a supposition that is inferred from behavior. In contrast to humans, however, in general, animals do not appear to be self-aware. Perhaps the most dramatic demonstration of the latter fact is that animals are unresponsive to their own image in a mirror (after, perhaps, an initial 'second-take' that quickly fades). We will have much to say about self-awareness in the next chapter. Here the goal is to achieve a feel for the profound intertwining of consciousness and memory. Many brain-injured patients show major alterations of general awareness. In the past, much patient behavior attributed to memory loss may have in fact been indicative of a confused state resulting from modified consciousness and defective memory retrieval.

It is instructive to examine what is remembered. Of course, by definition, certain details about the subject event, place, idea or object are recorded. The documented information may be quite abstract, and more will be said about that below. But in addition to details relevant to the item recalled, the recollection directly references the being who is remembering. Thus, every recalled image also includes, either explicitly or implicitly, a basic relationship to the being who is remembering. If I imagine what it felt like to jump in a hot tub or to experience a sunburn, I certainly am referencing myself. I actually feel a relationship to the recalled subjects, rather than just view an image. The cited examples were rather personal, so maybe the presence within the memory of a relationship to myself is not surprising. But even with recollections that are not so personal, the self-reference is also present. A similar feeling of identity is still there if I recall, for instance, a professional sporting event or movie viewed on television. The object of the memory, and my sense of how I felt about the event at the time, are basically inseparable. Even when I recall something from long ago, the total mental experience always includes my feelings about or physical relationship to the item as well as details about the item itself.

It is critical to distinguish between the latter concept of self-reference and the notion of self-consciousness. Self-reference is purely a representation of one's own feelings that accompanies an individual memory, and provides a frame of reference to the body of the person remembering. We infer that many animal species exhibit self-reference in association with the surmised degree of consciousness. In stark contrast, self-consciousness refers to a being that is aware of being aware, an internal and yet third-person-like, detached (aloof) sense of conventional, first-person, ongoing awareness. Self-consciousness is what distinguishes humans from all other animals, and forms the subject of the next chapter.

Our inner world is purely subjective, being inaccessible to anyone else. Inaccessibility is, in fact, what makes consciousness so difficult to study. The brain creates a dynamic, continuous image of that part of the world targeted for current attention. The conscious image employs elements from present attention and past experience, both being analyzed in the setting of a bodily self-image as a frame of reference, to render analysis and interpretation. Of course, ties to the past directly depend on memory. Further, if the results are deemed important, details of the present moment are directed to memory for storage. New memories always include information on the relationship to the bodily frame of reference, to aid future interpretation. Employing such a dynamic, continuous reconciliation of present, past and benchmark reference, the brain formulates a conscious world of incredible richness. It is in the context of the relationship of the past and present to the host being that meaning is derived.

Memories go through a creation process, exist for prolonged periods in some stored state, and copies are retrieved (the original memory is left intact). Memory creation and retrieval are inextricably intertwined with consciousness. At least two types of memory are widely recognized, designated as short-term (looking up a phone number and remembering it long enough to dial the number) and long-term memory (recalling your residence address), respectively. Some have dissected short-term memory into one or more additional elements, but that is not of present concern.

Key players in the processes of memory (and in almost all other brain interactions) are connections between nerve cells called synapses. Nerve cells, or neurons, are basically polar, having an input and an output. In general, the inputs to neurons occur through connections directly to the main cell body or through connections to cell input extensions called dendrites. Neurons typically have just one output channel, a cell extension termed an axon. Importantly, the axon typically forms profuse branches at various points, and can therefore exert influence on innumerable other cells (about 10,000 connections per neuron, on average). The specialized zone of connection between neurons is termed a synapse. The synapse is a small and very narrow physical gap between distinct structural loci on the input axon terminal on one hand and the recipient dendrite or cell body on the other (advanced readers will also know that some dendro-dendritic and axo-axonic synapses exist as well, but such discussion would impose unnecessary complication here). Transmission along neurons is a propagated electrical response, while transmission across the minuscule gaps that constitute synapses is through chemical diffusion.

Short-term memory is a dynamic process. Short-term memory is believed encoded by virtue of temporary changes in the efficacy of synaptic transmission in a select group of cells, termed a cell assembly or cell net, unique to the subject memory. In fact, it is the temporary changes in the efficacy of synaptic transmission that determine those particular cells that are to form the transitory cell assembly. So, short-term memory is described as forming transient (up to several hours) cell assemblies or neural nets peculiar to the memory-destined data. This means that each impending memory involves activity in an exclusive assemblage of cells that are united for a few hours in the active process of temporarily sustaining the memory trace.

Short-term memory is an apparent necessity because it takes several hours to initiate the creation of long-term memory. A proper blow to the head within minutes after a memorable event eliminates long-term memory of the happening, but the same blow hours later has little effect. Once long-term memory has had a sufficient opportunity to form, the transitory cell assembly employed for short-term memory are believed to slowly disappear. The basis is that the temporary changes in synaptic transmission efficacy, which were instrumental in forming the transitory short-term memory cell assembly originally, gradually wear off.

Short-term memory therefore involves transient electrochemical events at many synapses. Given time and repetitive activity through the short-term memory net, the result is believed to be anatomical changes that become relatively permanent after short-term memory traces cease. The processes that build long-term memory are believed to include steadfast changes in the efficacy of certain synapses. In turn, this results in persistent, altered activity in select neural pathways. It is known that long-term memory is not located in a restricted place in the brain, and so the belief is that the enduring pathways are widely distributed. Therefore, each long-term memory has a dispersed nature that is also distinct from the distributed pattern of activity embodying any other memory.

Perceptual Filtering

We navigate our world by observing, learning (recording organized constructs), and recalling data for synthesis with ongoing happenings to mold immediate behavior. In general, we feel our view of the world is accurate and up to date.

Let's turn to vision as an example. If asked to describe our visual capabilities, few non-scientists would find fault with an assertion that we conduct ourselves and interact with the environment using viewed and remembered data that is accurate and timely. In contrast, most would be shocked if told that what we see or remember is in large part a fantasy. Yet, as developed below, the truth is that our immediate and past sense of the world seems to be a conceptual fabrication of profound proportions.

The following discussion addresses several successive layers of abstraction, imposed on our view of the world by the peripheral and central nervous system, that will be collectively termed perceptual filtering.

The Windows of Our Senses. Humans and the higher animals are typically ascribed six main senses: visual, auditory, tactile, taste, smell, and proprioceptive, respectively. Taste, smell, and most of the group of senses labeled tactile (touch, pressure, temperature, pain) are direct sensations, involving physical contact with something in the environment (taste; smell; tactile) or within the body itself (proprioceptive; e.g., our sense of limb position). The tactile group also exhibits representatives of non-contact sensation, such as the thermal and painful sense from concentrated radiant heat. Of course, vision and audition are generally sensory modalities of a non-contact nature.

But there are vast categories of data that our sensory systems ignore. For instance, out of the entire wavelength spectrum of electromagnetic radiation, we respond to but a tiny fraction. Vision employs only the very narrow band of visible light wavelengths, and part of our thermal sense responds uniquely to a select band of infrared wavelengths. Our auditory sense also is very exclusive, tuned to a narrow range of frequencies related to mechanical (sound) disturbances in air. Taste buds are drastically confined in sensibility to just four primary groups of chemical properties. Certain tactile senses are sparse in density and/or restricted to particular parts of the body, and so on. The elaboration of details could be greatly extended.

The point is that there is too much data rattling around the world. Even if an organism could continuously and accurately acquire all available information in real time (immediately), the task of meaningful analysis would be quite impossible. What proved to be a better strategy during evolution was the use of sampling. Our sensory systems have adapted to monitor a small number of critical physical parameters, and to sample each parameter at a rate that provides a reasonably useful abstraction of reality. We look at a complex world through a few carefully placed sensory windows, and ignore whatever else is happening. With respect to all other unsampled data, we are flying blind.

Sensory Pathways. Once the highly selected sensory information enters the nervous system, profound levels of additional selection occur. Light only enters the pupils from the direction we aim the eyes. Even then, only a portion of the photons in the incident light actually trigger photoreceptor cells in the retina. Those cells in turn are connected to a network of other cells in the retina that selectively extract certain detail, ignoring the remaining data. The result is that the information from 100 million photoreceptor cells is severely abstracted to enter only one million cells directing information from the retina further into the central nervous system. Information is further condensed at each of several successive processing centers in the thalamus of the mid-brain, the primary visual cortex (and other less mainstream pathways), and diverse secondary and tertiary cortical realms beyond.

Two issues are critical. At each succeeding brain center, information is extracted by combining and analyzing the data from the active groups of cells in different ways. Secondly, also at each brain center, new pathways arise, spreading the influence of the successively abstracted sensory information to more and more brain centers. Finally, at each relevant brain center, feedback from centers farther up the line and/or from other key brain centers exerts a gate keeping function on the information flow. Simplistically, of the many forms of information impinging on each successive center, data related to the immediate focus of attention, although highly processed as it passes through, is allowed to otherwise traverse the center relatively unimpeded. However, much other information is suppressed, to further reduce the amount of data that the highest levels of analysis and interpretation must digest.

Cortical Processing. The processes of successive abstraction and filtration presumably continue at the level of secondary and tertiary cortical regions.

But the extracted features of information become more and more abstract, to the point that it has not been possible to clearly delineate much of the actual processing. For example, the precise location of various features of a viewed object (spatial localization) is preserved through the retina, intermediate centers in the pathway to the visual cortex, and early centers within the visual cortex proper. But beyond that, the maintenance of spatial localization, seemingly so crucial in preceding stages, becomes more vague or is lost all together. Presumably, by the time significant processing has occurred in the visual cortical areas, all of the relevant spatial data has already been extracted and then recoded in some other way. Further processing of the image turns to more global abstractions such as shape, color and identity.

Consciousness. The still mysterious process by which the brain creates dynamic ongoing experience certainly adds further filtering effects. Consciousness can be viewed as the spotlight of attention, focusing awareness and interpretation on a highly restricted segment of available information. Also, memory imposes substantial filtering as well. We don't store every detail of every moment for three reasons: a) we can't, because much detail was discarded by perceptual filtering; b) we don't direct all moments to memory, but only a small fraction deemed critical for future reference); and c) for a moment that is to be stored, we generally only record key fragments of particular features deemed important relative to the current situational context.

We can gain another glimpse of the mind and its perceptual filtration through reflection on a common experience. It is rather amazing that a real scene (or photograph thereof) and a simple artist's sketch of the same scene evoke similar percepts. The reason for surprise is that the pattern of retinal activation for the two cases is strikingly different. The consensus here is that the brain extracts a select group of features from the field of view, in the process of perceptual filtration on the way to developing a percept. Apparently, the percepts are quite similar for a scene versus a skeleton sketch thereof. The implication is that the features extracted in normal perception closely resemble elements of the sketch.

As an illustration, up to and including the visual cortex, early processing focuses on scene primitives (feature extraction) such as edges, bars, blobs and line ends. The latter information is augmented by data relative to contrast, orientation, width, length, and position. All of these features are largely processed separately, however. Then, subsequent processing begins to reconstruct an abstraction of the sketch, assembling element relationships, the rendering of a two-dimensional sketch, and finally a full three-dimensional representation.

The general concept of feature extraction fits very well with two issues discussed previously: a) the independently discovered modular structure of the cortex (cortical columns); and b) the many mindlets model of mental functioning. The modules, cylindrical ensembles of cells carrying out one kind of analysis, are certainly consistent with a conceptual architecture of feature processing. Higher level modules or ensembles of such processing units would then seem to be reasonable candidates for even more elaborate analyses on successively more elevated planes of abstraction.

An Overview of Consciousness

So the mind uses outlines, edges, blobs and so forth, to construct a simulation of the world. And if the collection of features and attributes is incomplete relative to the realization of a context-meaningful interpretation, the mind manages anyway. For example, we fall prey to optical illusions due to the brain making certain assumptions to render consistent an otherwise incomplete object or scene. Simply, if holes are encountered in the information, the mind merely fills in the gaps in a fashion to best make sense of the available data. In fact, the mind must improvise all the time, due to ubiquitous perceptual filtering. When environmental data is incomplete to some degree, the mind must ad-lib even more. The fact that our actions are usually so remarkably appropriate is a supreme testament to evolution's efficient development of perceptual filtration and abstraction mechanisms.

In summary, we stumble through the world in perhaps a surprisingly indirect way. Like the blind man using his cane, we explore the world in a highly select manner through our narrow windows of sense. The data received is crunched and crunched again and again to extract a vastly compressed, highly abstracted set of information. Then, the mind combines the processed data, draws on memory to benefit from experience, gleans further meaning through the body frame of reference, fills in gaps in the data using educated guesses, and renders a hypothesis of reality upon which we act. For each species, evolution has selected that group of features to best get by, with the least cost to the organism in terms of mental processing.

Consciousness is an incredible demonstration of the ultimate power of self-organization. But consciousness is not the pinnacle of self-organized processing. Humans have surpassed the realm of even our closest genetic relatives by an enormous chasm that has changed forever the course of evolution on earth. And it is to the crowning achievement of humans, the development of self-consciousness, that we next turn our conscious focus.

Chapter 6

The Sudden Rise of Self-Consciousness

The Tenacious Self

Lying deep within our consciousness is a strong sense of personal identity. As we advance through infancy, childhood, the teenage years, and stages of adulthood, our attitudes, beliefs, behavior and numerous other attributes change. Yet we possess a tenacious conviction that we are one and the same person throughout. But what is the inner essence that is really us? It is the self.

We view other people in a manner entirely distinct from the way we picture ourselves. Our image of others is usually of their general physical structure first, and then their personality. Conversely, our view of ourselves is really dual in nature as well, but split along dimensions of body and mind.

A person usually likens their own body to a possession, feeling the body is controlled and, essentially, owned. However, we think of our mind not as another bodily object or function, not as a possession, but as being the real us. An individual may loose limbs, be paralyzed from the neck down, or be subjected to countless other atrocities of the body, but the mind and the self survive intact — perhaps with a different perspective and personality — but intact. If full consciousness is retained, the self is not diminished in magnitude by non-cerebral bodily losses or impairments.

God is a mind! At least, that is what virtually all religions teach. In terms of the human mind, the view of many religions, especially of Western persuasions, is that the essence of a person is their soul (essentially, mind). The issue of the soul will be addressed later, especially in Chapter 8. For now, the focus is to explore the relation of self to mentation (all mental activity, collectively; cognition) and structure.

On introspection, our mental life seems detached, disembodied. Nevertheless, mentation is tightly coupled to the physical world in two ways: a) the mind receives inputs via the senses; and b) elicits change in the body and physical world through volition. A controversy has raged for centuries about the relationship between the mind (soul) and the body (in modern terminology, the brain). Is the mind a disembodied thing existing in a unique space free from the laws of nature? Or can the mind be totally resolved in terms of brain activity? The latter conundrum serves as the main topic of the next chapter.

But back to the question of what is the self? Maybe we can fashion an envelope around our ghostly immaterial inner being by reviewing some key facts. As developed in the last chapter, we are not always the same person from one moment to the next. Among various competing mindlets, a new commander frequently rises to the forefront, often suddenly and without warning. In the process, our thoughts, actions, and personality can change. Usually, the changes are smooth and diplomatic. However, if fatigued or under stress, we sometimes lose control.

Nevertheless, through all the turmoil, we staunchly foster the belief that we are more unified and consistent than we really are. In spite of the drastically different agendas of our individual competing mindlets, as even casual intro-spection will verify, we maintain a deep feeling of continuity and orderliness. The percept of unity can be viewed as a product of just another one of our inner mindlets, the self, having the same type of limited role and insight as the other singular mindlets. The comforting sensation of harmony and unity is an illusion of limited perspective.

Cognitive scientists have found that the self is concerned more with emo-tion than rational thought. Evolution apparently developed the self as a senti-nel, interpreting everything encountered in terms of relative threats to the being. The self emotionally assesses individual changes in the external environment, and evaluates what course of action seems most appropriate, whether attack, approach, observation, flight, or whatever. Humans have learned to override the crude reflexive responses characteristic of our animal ancestors, but the underlying function of the system seems to be basically the same.

In other words, through evolution, the self has become the principal rapid appraisal and response system. To assure immediate reactions, the self directly connects to certain ingrained automatic response patterns, the emotions, which prepare and motivate imperative action. The main loci of the self include: a) the frontal lobe of each cerebral hemisphere; and b) the limbic system, a round area at the base of the cerebrum and surrounding the mid-brain (an elaboration sitting atop the upper end of the brain stem). There is much more to emotions than simple extremes such as outbursts or panic reactions. And emotions have much more to do with guiding our ongoing actions than most of us realize.

Emotions are considered to be so prominent because they are quite func-tional and have been around a very long time. Countless studies have superbly documented comparative brain structure and significant knowledge about func-tion and behavior in species at all levels of complexity, and the fossil record has contributed substantial insight as well. It has been found that the limbic system first developed long ago when the dominant animals were very dependent upon smell and had comparably poor senses of sight and hearing. Since then, the relative capabilities of the visual, tactile and auditory systems have far out paced the still somewhat primitive limbic system. The latter developments have been paralleled by the prodigious elaboration of the cerebrum. The new sensory systems and the rest of the cerebrum in general are more obvious and easy to study, and exhibit far more spectacular performance in terms of coherent nervous activities, precise topological mapping of the environment, and rapid conduction properties. But it is clear from studies in animals and especially in humans with selected brain injuries or disease that the modern embodiment of certain primitive brain areas imposes substantial control on our being and our sense of being.

Self-Consciousness Defined

The concept was introduced previously that consciousness extends down the animal evolutionary tree to some extent. The exact prevalence of consciousness is not important for present discussion. The important issue is that consciousness is not a threshold phenomenon, released only after some high level of cerebral function is manifest. Rather, consciousness is believed by most workers in the brain sciences to appear gradually as species complexity is ascended, in accord with a direct but inexact function of brain complication and intricacy.

The opposite may be true of self-consciousness. As described earlier in the current chapter, self-consciousness — that is, consciousness of being conscious — seems to have abruptly arisen with the advent of humans or perhaps their most immediate predecessors. Here, sudden appearance is to be taken in terms of a time scale compatible with the evolution of successive near-human species. Even so, in the overall perspective of geologic time, the interval since ancestral humans first walked the earth is an eye blink.

Some insight of the human self can be obtained by realizing that we humans enjoy an unusual capability: we know what we know. This is at least one step removed from the primal experience of seeing, hearing, acting, and reacting. The vast number of studies of innumerable species at all levels of complexity have failed to reveal sound evidence that any non-human animal is self-conscious. The only possible exceptions, and any apparent capabilities are quite weak by human standards, are select representatives of the higher primates. A brief review of evolutionary development of the brain is warranted.

How does the human brain compare to that of other animals, past and present? Briefly, the mainstream of present understanding depicts the development of brain function as follows. The key to brain evolution is believed more related to structure than to size. The brain stem began as a coordinating enlargement at the head end of the spinal cord, and has since dramatically expanded. The most archaic structures, such as the brain stem, appear today as the highest structure in primitive species like sharks and lampreys. The midbrain, a major enlargement enveloping the upper brain stem, evolved later, and remains the highest structure in most fish and amphibians. The limbic system and cerebrum appeared even later in evolution, and today are the dominant structures in mammals. The higher mammals developed last, and today feature elaborate cerebral cortices and high intelligence.

A key evolutionary driving force for the development of the cortex and associated structures may have been hefty advantages afforded by abilities to permanently represent (to model) the environment within the mind. In certain demanding niches, an internal model of the relevant environment would convey substantial survival value to any species possessing such previously unprecedented powers.

How do the animals of the present compare to those of the past? Importantly, large numbers of animals exist today that have as their dominant brain function each of the four structural groups identified above. Significantly, comparative neuro-anatomy reveals that, through evolution, the newer systems have been grafted onto the older structures. In other words, earlier systems have been retained, perhaps with somewhat modified function, as brain design has advanced. Brain evolution, as does evolution of living and even non-living matter in general (see Part I), has been found to build on what was previously available, rather than starting over to design a new class of brain. Thus, the brain of more complicated beings is organized in interrelated layers, in an onion-skin fashion, the tiers documenting in an approximate way the stages of evolutionary history.

To clarify the above historical evolutionary model further, primitive reflex systems were the basis of sub-mammalian animals, and depended on structures and functions of the brain stem. Later, instinctual drives and simple associative conditioning evolved along with the mid-brain and limbic structures. Animals limited to such brain system complements are represented by birds and lower mammals. Distinctly more advanced representational systems evolved even more recently, and are exemplified by higher mammals. Finally, in the last moment of geologic time, self-consciousness appeared as another distinct manifestation of the endlessly progressing functional and structural hierarchy of central neural processing.

Pursuing the latter statement, the highest level of function, what we have termed self-consciousness, has been found by cognitive scientists in a primordial form in certain of the great apes, and, as the most developed mind representational form on earth, in humans. The electrifying new accomplishment, in part, is the ability to selectively direct attention not only to observed activity or elements recalled from memory, but also, in an aloof, parallel mode, to introspectively 'watch' such ongoing traditional mentation. For instance, I can 'watch' myself driving — I can somehow intentionally induce a second conscious state (or, perhaps split my primary conscious state in two), where I can continue driving with one state and watch myself drive from the other. The second conscious state is some kind of aloof, seemingly superior vantage point that conveys at least the illusion of independence, and that can judge and even influence my primary ongoing actions. However, in my own introspective experience, the second conscious state does not allow me to do two activities at once, and otherwise does not appear capable of actually inducing any outside action except through an influence on primary consciousness. By extrapolation, I assume everyone else has the same capability, although it may be less developed in many people due to lack of direct use.

The brain is composed of layer upon hierarchical layer of structure and of functional abstraction developed through untold episodes of self-organization. The primary visual system pathway will arbitrarily be used to demonstrate both concepts. First, structural layering can be dramatically seen in the successive brain centers that incoming data successively traverses:

    a) three retinal processing stages;

    b) a specific center in the thalamus;

    c) in order, the primary, secondary and tertiary visual cortices; and

    d) beyond, to other associative processing.

Second, functional abstraction is illustrated by the basic image attributes that are the focus of processing in the various primary visual pathway centers:

    a) the retina sorts data as to color (via cone receptors) and relative to field size and intensity (rod receptors), among other functions;

    b) the thalamic center and the primary and secondary visual centers conduct processing that selectively pulls out data relative to edges, arcs, and other primitives of a scene; and

    c) the tertiary visual cortex and other associative centers emphasize final identification and interpretive aspects of the sense to derive meaning and response. Both structural and functional hierarchical details fill bookshelves in university libraries — the above descriptions are extremely simplistic but suffice to help make the point. The brain is highly hierarchical, regardless of the dimension used for analysis, whether structural, functional, or even histological, biochemical, or electrophysiological.

At a very recent stage, the leading wave front of brain evolutionary development apparently exceeded some threshold, permitting self-consciousness to suddenly flourish. Self-consciousness is yet another hierarchical layer (level) of function that earth bound mentation has achieved. A threshold is believed to be involved due to the sudden appearance of self-consciousness on an evolutionary time scale.

The exact processes and mechanisms of self-consciousness are still incompletely understood. However, one suggestion, in my opinion quite likely to represent major truth, is that we are witness to another emerging property, a new brain processing capability dependent upon functional interplay between different hierarchical levels of brain processing. Somehow, the higher mental levels may be able to impose independent, objective, parallel monitoring and control on the inputs and mechanisms of mentation at lower levels of processing. In any case, the brain has achieved a level of abstraction that finally allows continuous internal self-observation of ongoing traditional conscious mentation.

Comparisons of Humans with the Higher Apes

The capabilities of human self-consciousness have exploded over the time since we broke away from our common ancestors with the great apes. Three discrete stages in the development of truly human cognition are to be described in the next section. But it is important first to lay some groundwork.

There are a number of dimensions that might be employed to illuminate the differences between higher apes and humans. Some parameters provide better differentiation than others. For example, the differences are as little as two percent when the genetic blueprints of the closest apes and humans are compared. However, the cognitive differences between the higher apes and man are striking. We will see that a powerful means to view cognitive ability is through the cultural features of a species. It turns out that culture is a particularly enlightening parameter in another way as well, because it seems to depend very closely on representational strategies of the mind (the form in which we code, view and manipulate data). Human memory employs many seemingly novel systems of representation, and the development of such systems will be shown to provide important insight in the eruptive developments distinguishing cognition in humans versus the higher apes.

As described previously, memory and consciousness seem to be inseparable. Three distinct types of memory can be recognized:

Procedural. Memory that is concerned with the learning of algorithms or schemas that underlie patterns of activity, without specific details of the immediate event; not being bound to exacting situations, the action patterns are available for wide use under varying circumstances;

Episodic. The key here is memory related to events or minor episodes (happenings); episodic memory is concrete, tightly bound to the details of the immediate situation, and unreflective; events or minor composites of multiple events (limited episodes, or happenings) are the highest level of representation of episodic memory, so that generalization to situations varying significantly in character is unlikely; and

Semantic. This form of memory is symbolic in nature, and is amenable to pronounced generalization; thus, semantic memory is not tightly restricted to the situation, and affords the lucky possessor a tremendous advantage in flexibility.

The three identified types of memory thus typify distinct representational strategies of the mind for encrypting objects, processes or relationships.

Procedural memory has been found to be structurally and historically the most primitive. Simple organisms can learn to execute patterns of action without high dependence on precise situational recall. Ambulation necessarily involves procedural memory, because the situations where ambulation is appropriate are diverse for most animals, and one style, cadence and stride would not do. Procedural memory is best at preserving generalities of action, and is basically the opposite of episodic memory with its emphasis on event specifics, such as typing. In recording the universality of action, procedural memories are really compelled to ignore situation specifics, to avoid confounding the information beyond sense.

As an example, one must learn the generalities (a procedural memory) of properly returning a tennis volley, rather than memorizing an exact routine, because no two situations are exactly the same. Episodic recall would interfere with versatility. On the other hand, a professional dancer must employ episodic memory in the act of learning and executing the details of a precise complicated routine. In parallel, both the tennis player and the dancer will also employ procedural memories to execute many universal reaction movements (e.g., maintaining balance).

Procedural and episodic memory have been shown to involve distinct neural mechanisms. By way of a simple illustration, a brain lesion in one specific brain area of particular birds will selectively block song behavior, a procedural memory system. In turn, a lesion in a different area of the same bird species will block behavior associated with hiding and locating food, an episodic memory routine. Neither lesion blocks the alternative function.

Both procedural and episodic memory systems appear to be represented in a wide spectrum of animals, including birds and mammals. Yet the two memory strategies seem to have evolved separately and for different reasons. Procedural memories have been found to record generalities and disregard specifics. Alternatively, episodic memories have been found to register specifics and neglect generalities. For perspective, a neural mechanism that rejected both generalities and specifics wouldn't accomplish much at all, and a technique that tried to accomplish both might end up overwhelmed.

It has been found that episodic memory is more developed in apes than in any other species. Apes are alert to subtleties of social and pragmatic situations to which other species appear unaware. Still, episodic memory is an integral part of the mentation of a wide range of species, the relative potency varying with general evolutionary advancement. Also, episodic memory is deemed to require at least some level of consciousness. In contrast, lower animals confined to procedural memories are basically stimulus-response automatons, with little ability to adapt to changing situations not programmed in procedural protocols.

On the other hand, in humans, episodic memory is found subservient to the dominant information store, that of semantic memory. Semantic memory is symbolic in nature, and the nearest analog in animals may be the training of certain apes to use a rudimentary sign language. However, even apes trained to use signs or visual symbols do not appear capable of mastering large sets of symbolic information or using such data in complicated abstractions. A human infant that has begun to speak has already surpassed the highest achievements of apes.

In summary, apes represent the penultimate advancement of the episodic mind. Many animals are quite adept in event perception and episodic storage, but apes are the grand achievers. Apes exhibit an increased capacity for representation of the self and are superior problem solvers compared to other mammals. Our nearest relatives, chimpanzees, possess a complex social structure that is quite demanding relative to requirements for event perception and episodic memory. But the shortcoming is a poor ability to recall and reanalyze a situation from different perspectives. Not having symbolic representational abilities, even the chimpanzee cannot accomplish the level of abstraction and its attendant increased adaptive flexibility available to the human.

The distinction between humans and the highest apes is monumental. Episodic memory appears to be unique to birds and mammals, and its ability to adapt is believed to be superior to procedural memories. In turn, the human manifests all three information storage strategies, but by far the dominant type is semantic memory. Further insight regarding the huge evolutionary leap that semantic memory has afforded is the subject of the next section.

The Explosive Yet Staged Ascent of Humans

There are a number of theories regarding the mental differences between apes and humans, and how the divide was bridged. But our main thrust would be subverted by an in-depth side trip to explore alternatives. Important here is a feeling for the true nature of the ape versus human gulf that was crossed, and, especially, significant insights to broaden our grasp of consciousness. Critically, even though the mental gap between apes and humans is wide, it does not appear at all unmanageable through conventional evolution. In particular, there is no reason for or utility in assuming some form of divine intervention.

The ape-to-human abyss is wide enough that the occurrence of one single innovation is an unlikely explanation. We will build on a more reasonable working hypothesis, a series of cultural and representational stages of change that, it will be shown, demonstrate one rational approach to progressively bridge the gap in smaller, more plausible steps. Notably, in terms of the normal time scale of evolution, the conversions occurred in rapid succession.

For coherence and brevity, the following discussion recounts an interpretation of human ascent from the recent theory proposed by Merlin Donald (*Origins of The Modern Mind*). Donald employs diverse mainstream evidence and some personal interpretation to develop a modern hypothesis regarding the rise of humans. Donald's model, which is a strong contending theory on its own, also serves for our purposes to highlight important aspects of consciousness and self-consciousness that must be met by any successful theory.

Donald proposes three fundamental innovations leading from ape to humans. Relevant aspects of each stage are briefly reviewed below, and are also represented diagrammatically in Fig. 6.1. It should be realized that only his main ideas and conclusions are emphasized here. Huge amounts of supporting evidence and interpretive discussion have been omitted so that we don't get sidetracked from our overall purpose.

Mimetic Culture. As described previously, the higher primates represent the epitome of development of the episodic mind. The first break from episodic cultures (Fig. 6.1A) proposed by Donald is termed mimetic culture. For background, the earliest hominid species found in the evolutionary record (*Australopithecus afarensis*) arose in Africa about 4 million years ago. The remains of *afarensis* show no evidence deviating from an ape-like episodic culture. Later, on the order of 1.5 to 2 million years ago, the appearance of *Homo habilis* began to reveal glimmers of change, but still no pronounced discontinuity with the episodic system. However, about 1.5 million years ago, *Homo erectus* surfaced, exhibiting the capacity to manufacture relatively complicated tools. *Erectus* representatives spread over the entire Eurasian continent demonstrating new and impressive social and technical skills of survival in diverse habitats. The evident capabilities of *erectus* were far beyond the reach of earlier hominids.

Mimetic culture is viewed as a stepping stone, a missing link, proposed as a means to set the stage for the later advances to follow. However, it is critical to note that the hypothesized developments of mimetic culture discussed here (or any alternative explanations in the literature) are not viewed as happening by way of a grand plan building toward human language. As always, evolution was diligent in exploration and experimentation, but mindless.

The essence of the mimetic hypothesis (mime-like mental constructs) is founded on the ability to generate conscious, self-launched, mental representations that are willful but not linguistic. The advance is from internal representation of happenings or *events* (the episodic mind) to the superior representation of full, enriched *episodes* (extended spatio-temporal amalgams of individual events). Donald's definition is rigorous, and carefully excludes a host of other behaviors. The new capability, Mimesis, according to Donald, was the advent of understanding and practicing imitation, a breakthrough realization that objects, processes or relationships could be represented by substitute actions or thoughts. Imitation could also be used by the organism itself to re-enact and reanalyze material. In short, the new capability conveyed the ability to rethink, but was still short of being symbolic. The reason is that recalled images were still considered representations of original events, since no symbols were as yet employed.

Mimesis is widely evident in humans today, and is characterized by many actions and modalities. Physical expressions, vocal tones, eye movement patterns, postures, gestures and various groupings of such elements into much more complex behaviors are common components of communications or even expression to oneself.

Profound social consequences become possible with the introduction of mimesis. Short term benefits could include communications about issues of immediate importance, based on primitive versions of the modern mimetic elements listed in the prior paragraph. Also, mimesis would provide the basis for the beginnings of shared, enduring knowledge, through similar mimetically-based systems of social interaction. In turn, shared knowledge would make possible rapid social evolution and the development of more elaborate technology (e.g., tools) and techniques (e.g., hunting strategies).

Dramatic changes in the brain are proposed in association with the development of mimetic culture. Donald proposes the advent of a new representational mode based on mimesis, and a new brain system termed the 'mimetic controller' (Fig. 6.1B) that integrates abstractions from the self and from event perception to realize a still higher level of abstract representation. The essence of the mimetic controller is seen as an advance in the self-conscious capabilities that first began in the higher apes. Two key features were an improved image of the body and its actions in space, and better abilities to represent stored information to oneself, early hints of the emerging new capability of self-consciousness. In Donald's view, episodic systems were still present and important, but gradually came to play a supporting role to the blossoming mimetic controller.

Mythic Culture. The reign of *Homo erectus* lasted until about 300,000 years ago. Between the decline of erectus and the rise of modern humans about 50,000 years ago exists a long, poorly understood transition. The lack of insight is primarily due to the dearth of archeological data. Much of that interval was the time of the Neanderthals in Europe. The Neanderthals were once felt likely to be involved in the lineage leading to modern humans. More recent evidence and interpretations, however, relegate Neanderthals to a dead end evolutionary path. Although detractors exist, the current consensus is that modern humans evolved prior to and in parallel with Neanderthals.

Archeological records of modern humans, *Homo sapiens sapiens*, first appear about 125,000 years ago in Africa. Also, *sapiens* appear in European, Asian and Australian remains from about 45,000 years ago, and records in the Americas indicate a presence covering at least the most recent 25,000 years.

The transition interval from 400,000 to 50,000 years ago is cloudy, and much remains to be resolved. However, by 50,000 years ago, the clearly dominant species was *Homo sapiens sapiens*, and the characteristic cultural system was aboriginal. Humans now had a modern appearance, and culturally displayed movements toward more organized and larger social structures. Language was also present.

The developments that must have occurred between the mimetic culture and the earliest human cultures were dramatic. The early humans prepared food, had developed the production of clothing, constructed shelters, and transported heavy objects. They also had an extensive social and religious life, a primitive political system, and employed decorative items.

The fundamental elements of the mind were present as well, the brain was as large as it is today, and the basic structures of the contemporary cerebrum were in place. Inhabitants exhibited thought, group decision making, an elaborate language including grammar, and significant technical skills.

In terms of mind representational capabilities, Donald proposes that humans had achieved yet another major advance in capability and associated structure, mythical thought. The latter is a unified system of explanations and behavior-governing metaphors, or myths, to model the subject's world. Mind had expanded beyond the episodic perception of *events* and even past the mimetic reconstruction of extended *episodes*, to a detailed abstract modeling (a set of *myths*) of the subject's entire world. The goal was to explain observed nature and experience in a seemingly causal fashion, permitting the illusion of prediction and control.

The proposal is that the mind had developed to a point that explanations were required for why things happened the way that they did. In turn, since science did not as yet exist, individuals and societies collectively filled in gaping voids of understanding with myths, to render, within their limited view, a complete description of nature.

The progressive development of the capacity of speech and of language are argued by Donald to be paramount ingredients in the transition from mimetic to mythic culture. The exact selective pressures that resulted in evolution of the modern vocalization anatomy and the neural architectures for language have not as yet been accurately defined. However, the origin of language seems to have been driven first by the benefits of collective thought and synthesis brought forward by the emerging mythical mind. All aboriginal societies studied, whether the few still existing on earth today or those studied indirectly through the archeological record, display pronounced signs of a deep mythical life. Later, the further development of language and speech led to other phenomenal proficiencies and functions, including new forms of social and political organizations, the teaching of skills to others, and improved coordination of activities.

Myth appears to have been the first truly integrative protocol of the mind. The mythical mind brought together diverse elements of the present and past, both in on-line and re-analysis modes, to create a broad spatial and temporal framework for data processing and resolution. Interpretation was fulfilled, even in the absence of complete information, through the generation of pragmatic metaphors (mythical explanations) derived from collective experience.

To carry Donald's development further, the extraordinary cultivation of language not only brought the capacity for vocalized communications, but an entirely novel system for representing reality. New types of memory store were required. At this stage, Donald models cognition as governed by a new brain and mind structure, the linguistic controller (Fig. 6.1C). The linguistic controller assumes ultimate command, so even the mimetic controller is subservient. Characteristically, as found everywhere in evolution, new systems are grafted onto the previous architecture, so that the old brain centers and relationships are retained as well.

In actual operation, the new linguistic controller is envisioned as receiving direct inputs from both the episodic and mimetic controllers, producing representational products that are narrative models of the outer and inner worlds. Narrative thought is envisioned as the normal, automatic business of the linguistic controller. The result is the production of oral-verbal commentary on experience in a fashion as easily as the mimetic system generates representations in the form of action patterns. The linguistic controller serves as the ultimate governing function of the mythic stage of mind evolution.

The mythic mind is proposed to have rapidly moved cognition in the direction of knowledge consolidation and integration. The scattered, tangible mental ensemble of mimetic mind evolved into an integrated system of (largely illusory) causal interpretation. Myth is also taken to have represented the appearance and blossoming of symbolism, a stunning achievement in the relentless progression of mental abstraction. Finally, a pivotal role in the control of attention was assumed by the language system. The propensity for rehearsal afforded by linguistic thought permitted rapid access to memory and for memory to be cued in an anticipatory fashion. The result was an ever advancing substrate for conscious manipulation of the mental modeling process (thought and imagery), and therefore improved real-world flexibility of performance and insight.

Theoretic Culture. The final evolutionary stage described by Donald is the advent of theoretic culture. This represents yet another proposed fundamental reorganization of mind and its neural underpinnings. The creation of three vital cognitive phenomena underlying current human mentation are envisioned as the core transition from mythic to theoretic culture. These changes have all occurred very recently, within no more than the last few thousand years:

Graphic Invention. The mind has undergone a spectacular reversal in the relative importance of two primary sensory systems; mythic culture was primarily verbal symbolism, so the auditory system was emphasized; but with the recent emergence of written symbolic language, the visual system suddenly was thrust to center stage and visual representations came to reign; in a sense, but on a much more advanced level, this represents a return to the visual dominance of the episodic and mimetic minds;

External Memory. Mythic culture depended heavily on the internal memory of each individual; but modern humans are much more dependent upon external memory systems, including writing, graphic symbols, pictures, and diagrams; the architecture of the mind (e.g., visual memory; symbolic memory; mental processing) had to change to accommodate the new mode of integrated internal and external symbolic thinking;

Theory Construction. Finally, the most momentous contemporary change in mentation is the acquisition of a new thought product termed a theory; the modern mind has two different modes of thinking; one is narrative thought, a descendent of mythic culture heavily involved in today's literary arts; in contrast, analytic thought is a modern invention characteristic of such fields as law, government and science; argument, discovery, proof and theoretical synthesis are mainstays of analytic thought, the penultimate being an integrated theory that not only explains but also predicts.

These three specializations are, singly and collectively, remarkable in power and exciting in impact. What is truly new is a dramatic move from mind-centric cognition to a startling dependence on external media and mechanisms. Myth and narrative strategies model events by attaching meaning and establishing links using analogies. In stark contrast, theory dissects, analyzes, derives relationships, defines laws and relationships, and sets rules for the derivation, verification and analysis of information. The first step in analytic thought is to strip the object of all mythical content, to provide an open field for objective examination.

Mythic (aboriginal) cultures predominated until recently, and some primitive mythic societies persist today. Furthermore, even in post-industrial society, remnants of our mythical heritage are widely evident. As an example, all religious beliefs had their origins in the mythic mind that craved explanations. More recently, theoretic culture has progressively encroached on myth-based mentation and discourse, successively assuming previously mythical functions and roles. Theoretic culture has now been developing for several thousand years, and today has become the primary protocol of human thought.

The earlier transitions from episodic to mimetic and from mimetic to mythic minds were different in character from the most recent mythic to theoretic transition. The prior transformations were heavily dependent on changes to the nervous system and, in the case of the mythic, to substantial voice box structural evolution. But the transition from mythic to theoretic mind depended not only upon neurological change, but also heavily on technological invention. Theoretic culture was coded externally in writings and other external representations from the beginning, so that mentation and memory now extended in a very real sense beyond the confines of the mind. This would demand, yet again, major changes in cognitive architecture to better avail the newfound cognitive aids (see Fig. 6.1D).

Donald calls on several stages where the mental protocol underwent significant change, at least in key areas of the main sensory and perceptual pathways. How could the mind change structurally in just the right way to create the required substrate for a new mental protocol? Actually, this question is probably framed incorrectly. What is more likely is that behavior or culture changed first, initially in perhaps a very minor way. Nevertheless, if the change was advantageous to individual performance, and therefore, at least weakly improved survival and reproductive success, evolution took over. Through the incessant selective pressures of evolution, individuals more adapted in neural architecture to the emerging protocol would come to form a larger and larger share of the total population. If the driving force (the advantage of the new protocol) was strong enough, given enough time and sufficient generations, the entire population would be restructured. In addition, further advancement would continue to be compounded for as long as the driving force retained meaningful strength.

Our Perplexing Sense of Time

All of the fundamental equations of physics are symmetrical in time. One can describe processes proceeding in the backward direction (into the past) with equal ease compared to calculations concerning action in the forward direction (into the future). The reversal of the direction of time has no effect on solutions and predictions. This profound result seems completely at odds with our personal sense of being immersed in flowing time.

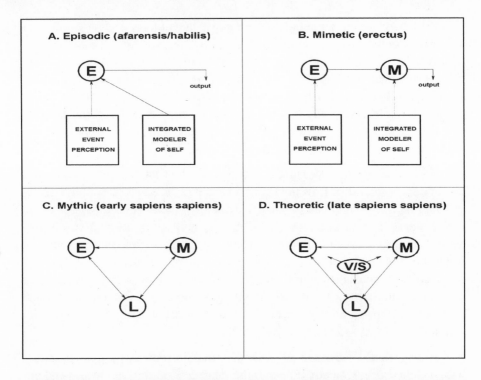

Figure 6.1. Schematic depiction of the emergence of new hierarchical representational and control functions in the mind that are distinctly human (adapted from Donald, *Origins of the Modern Mind*). Each newly appearing representational system is considered capable of modeling the outputs of subordinate systems.

A. The episodic mind of primates (and also Australopithecus aferensis, and probably Homo habilis) is primarily envisioned as driven by a superior external event perception system, the hallmark of primates. Influences of the Self-based representational functions were present but secondary.

B. The mimetic mind of Homo erectus features a Self representational system with much increased power, compared to representations associated with external event perception. Also, a new control system, hierarchically superior to the Episodic Controller (E), is postulated. The new system, the Mimetic Controller (M), receives inputs from both the episodic system and the Self. The Mimetic Controller represents the highest representational system in the mimetic mind.

Note that, to simplify the graphics, Figs. 6.1C and 6.1D represent the total repertoire of episodic and mimetic systems as simply a circled (E) and (M), respectively.

C. The advent of the mythic mind of early Homo sapiens sapiens is so distinct as to imply another major change in mental structure, and the emergence of yet another hierarchically super-ordinate system, the Linguistic Controller (L). The Linguistic Controller represents the most superior representational system in the mythic mind, and features the development of language in aboriginal cultures.

D. Finally, although beyond the scope of the present text, a system designated as the Visio-Symbolic (V/S) Controller is illustrated. Beyond the aboriginal culture of the mythic mind, Donald describes three more stages of human development. The final result, once all three of the latter mental advancements were in place as of a few thousand years ago, was Theoretic Culture.

And there are further paradoxes. As a case in point, the Theory of Relativity teaches that there is no universal 'now' for all observers. Depending on their relative velocities and positions in space, the now for one observer may be the past, present or future of a second observer. Such effects come into play as velocities become very high. However, here on earth, we don't encounter noticeable anomalies in day-to-day life. The relative velocities of most events on earth are so slow (relative to the speed of light) that we all share basically the same now.

We can also gain a measure of relief about the first paradox cited above, that of our sense of time flow not being revealed in the equations of physics, by considering the Second law of Thermodynamics (the Second Law) discussed in Chapter 3. Except processes occurring at equilibrium, all real world processes are non-symmetric, in that entropy (disorder) is irreversibly produced. Therefore, the increase in entropy associated with practical, real world interactions serves as a means to identify the forward direction of time. If I drop a light bulb on the floor, the order in the original light bulb is lost, and, for all practical purposes, the process is irreversible (the same light bulb cannot be fully restored from the pieces).

But so what! We are still left with a glaring discrepancy between the timeless, or at best academically time-symmetrical, descriptions of physics and our profound sense of both a sweeping time and a prominent 'now.' Also, regarding the mind, our sensation of time is tightly intertwined with self-consciousness. But, incredibly, time is just not a prominent parameter in the rigorous mathematical descriptions of the world. What is going on here?

Time is not like other physical parameters, at least when considered in the context of the human mind. Our sense of time seems somehow more basic than length, weight, temperature or other properties of pragmatic objects and relationships. Time does not arise through the senses (unless, of course, we look at a clock), but is rather of internal origin. Nevertheless, introspection by the reader will almost certainly reveal a very deep feeling of the passage of time, an impression so prominent that it is likely the most fundamental element of ongoing, long-term experience. Time seems to be the supreme frame upon which we display and manipulate mental happenings.

It is instructive to momentarily return again to the topic of memory, in pursuit of a key link to the sense of time. As discussed previously, our very feeling of personal identity (self) is closely coupled to memory. Enduring experience is an absolute requirement for personal identity, because an individual existing for only one moment makes no sense. To be a person implies both continuity of experience and some form of temporal association, such as memory.

We can gain some insight by examining two groups of clinical conditions. Recall that memory is organized into both a short-term and a long-term component. Patients can be found that appear to be missing short-term memory but who retain the long-term stores (e.g., Korsakov's syndrome). Such patients exhibit serious deficits of self, show substantial indifference to ongoing experience, and have lost the sense of time. In contrast, other patients can be identified that seem to be missing long-term memory but who retain short-term memory processes. In general, such patients exhibit behavior that seems to lack both a sense of the present and a long-term point of view. The latter patients also show poor performance relative to deriving or assigning meaning to objects and/or events, and, again, display serious problems with the sense of time.

Blind people, by comparison with the visually normal, exhibit a quite rudimentary sense of time. The blind only sense bodily position and change, but lack ongoing dynamic inputs about the changing environment. Most dynamics are learned only after the fact, not during the occurrence. The blind still have a sense of the present, being able to define relationships between events occurring at different times. However, the sense of time is obviously abnormal and seems to pass very slowly.

So how do normal people appraise the passage of time? One hypothesis is that we derive our sense of time from the qualitative differences between memories (either past or recent) versus current experience. Our sense of time occurs within consciousness, which for humans, often operates at the enhanced level of self-consciousness. In turn, our self-consciousness is believed to involve a dynamic ongoing interpretive interplay between past memories, present experience (and therefore including short-term memory), and the self (including body image). This would place the sense of time inextricably within human self-consciousness.

A corroborating hint is that when we are really busy, when we are focused to the point that we are unaware of all but the most compelling outside disturbances, time seems to pass very quickly. Perhaps, under conditions of extreme attention constraint, self-consciousness is suppressed so that all activity can be allocated to normal consciousness. The latter idea is consistent with an arrangement where our time sense is tightly linked to self-consciousness. Time (and more data) will tell.

Compared to humans, animals do not possess a strong sense of time. Of course, my pets know exactly when it's time to eat, but that's a more basic response dependent upon hunger and daily hormonal and biochemical rhythms. Even the higher primates do not show evidence of a strong sense of time. It appears that the vital and imperative sense of time experienced by humans is related to the brain elaboration that brought us self-consciousness.

Mind versus Matter

We have traveled a long road, collecting certain features and propositions pertinent to consciousness and ultimately self-consciousness. It has been shown that neither consciousness nor self-consciousness are fully understood as yet. Nevertheless, considerable knowledge and ideas regarding the mind and its workings have been reviewed.

Importantly, care has been taken to define the terms consciousness (general awareness) and self-consciousness (awareness of being aware) rigorously, and to employ the words accurately throughout the developing discussion. One intriguing relation is that consciousness has proved to be a continuously emerging property of the mind, growing ever more potent as the animal evolutionary tree is ascended. In contrast, self-consciousness appears to exhibit a definite threshold, a very high level (in terms of earth life, at least) of brain complexity, that of human mentation, being prerequisite. Once the self-consciousness threshold was exceeded, it seems that explanations were suddenly demanded for the workings of the world and how we fit into the picture.

One burning question is certainly whether or not human self-consciousness can be explained in terms of brain function. This fascinating conundrum has been the subject of searing debate for centuries, and represents the topic to be explored in the next chapter.

Chapter 7
The Deceptive Mind-Body Problem

Definition of the Problem

Over the last few hundred years, one of the most bewildering and mystifying issues concerning mentation has been labeled the mind-body problem. The question can be stated quite clearly: how does the mind relate to the body? However, the study and discourse has been anything but clear. In fact, the matter has created massive upheaval and exhausting, often angry emotional controversy that has, for centuries, wallowed in seemingly insurmountable altercation.

The prior two chapters have summarized objective findings regarding the relation of mind to brain. Actually, stating the subject as the mind-body problem is somewhat of a misnomer, a remnant of earlier centuries when brain function was poorly understood and the seat of intelligence was obscure. There is no credible evidence whatsoever that the mind is functionally coupled (excepting quite slow blood-born chemical systems) to any other body element besides the brain. Thus, the mind-body problem reduces pragmatically to how the mind relates to the brain.

Three key facts perhaps provide insight over what has helped fuel the energized mind-body debate in recent centuries. First has been the historical lack of knowledge about the body, brain and mind. We have only come to a reasonable (albeit still incomplete) understanding of the body in the present century, the brain in the last few decades, and the mind more recently yet. Second, the mind-body problem lies at the intersection of philosophy, religion and science, disciplines that have not cross-fertilized effectively and whose members often do not converse well. Third, the mind-body problem is usually discussed in terms of ordinary language. However, not only is common language imprecise, but Western languages inherently presuppose a mind separate from the body.

The simple question of how the mind relates to the body spawns a number of related riddles. For example, is the mind separate from the body? If the mind and body are distinct things, how are they functionally and physically interconnected and how is coordination accomplished? Is coordination absolute, or only partial? Furthermore, how does the mind first link up to the body, and what happens to the mind after death?

Alternatively, if the mind and body are not separate entities, how can mind be explained in terms of bodily (brain) function? Is the mind more brain-like, or is the brain more mind-like? If mind does represent brain action, then what is the soul? Is it reasonable to accept the familiar view that the soul is distinct from the brain? In other words, can all mental function be explained by brain activity, or is there some disembodied function acting above or next to mind as well?

Does Mental Activity have a Physical Substrate?

This is not a book about philosophy and metaphysics. A departure to review the voluminous literature and the numerous theoretical positions propounded by advocates of various philosophies would detract from the present theme. However, the interested reader is directed to many excellent sources in the 'Suggested Readings' section at the end of the present volume. Suffice it to say that, simplistically, with regard to the mind-body problem, there have been two gigantic camps, dualism and monism. Dualists come in many flavors, but basically see the mind and body as being distinct entities or processes in some way. However, rigorous examination reveals all dualistic variations put forth to date as being flawed, some in glaring and others in more subtle ways (e.g., see Mario Bunge, *The Mind-Body Problem*).

Basically, most dualist argument is founded on the use of imprecise, unscientific language and/or ambiguous definitions. In the final analysis, key questions are really semantically sidestepped, the purported 'answers' merely sweeping the real questions back into a deeper, more remote level of obscurity (see later discussion for more detail). Thus, even given exhaustive pursuit both historically and in modern times, dualism has just not proven to be scientifically viable.

Several monistic positions are weak in science as well, but others are more enlightened. An essential point here is that any realistic doctrine regarding the mind-body problem must, as with every other issue of inquiry, squarely face scientific rigor. Historically, science was often viewed as an inconvenient nuisance, that could be countered with eloquent discourse even when such maneuvers conflicted with direct observation or proven fact. Such a misguided approach is seen today as barren and unacceptable. Science has amassed spectacular success, and dancing around known contradictions can no longer be condoned.

For present purposes, we will contrast three general materialistic views under the monism flag that highlight pivotal issues: eliminative, reductive and emergentist. As mentioned, all three are materialisms, meaning that the existence of the body (brain) is acknowledged and the mind-body question centers on how mentation relates to bodily (brain) structure and function.

Eliminative materialism carries a catastrophic weakness, in denying the existence of an element that is clearly essential. The central tenet of eliminative materialism is that there is no mental, that everything is material in the strictest sense. A refined version of eliminative materialism is behaviorism, which, in its most extreme form, refuses to deal with mental states and events at all. The organism and its stimulus-response behaviors are treated as a black box, and mental states and events are denied existence and eliminated from study. It is an astonishing fact that the behaviorist view became a dominant force in psychology during the better part of the twentieth century, and broadly stifled cognitive research in other disciplines as well. Fortunately, this sterile and destructive construct has fallen into serious disrepute.

Reductive materialism holds that the central nervous system is a physical entity distinguished from other physical systems only in complexity. Thus, an explanation of mentation should require only physical concepts and theories strictly in line with normal physics. In other words, reductive materialism claims that the brain is nothing but an aggregate of cells, and that a complete understanding of brain cells and their interactions would include all there is to know about the mental.

Finally, we turn to emergentist materialism. This system of thought takes the view that the whole is more than the sum of its parts. Mentation is considered to be the direct result of brain function, but the full knowledge of brain cells and their interplay is not enough for total understanding. The mind could not be explained using only a wiring diagram of the brain and the knowledge of how various types of neurons work and influence other neurons. Mentation is viewed as an emerging property of cell aggregates, interacting in special ways that bring forth new properties and rules which are not inherently obvious.

The contention by reductionists that the actions of the mind are nothing but cell interactions is seductive but probably false. We saw in the previous detailed discussion of emerging properties (Chapter 2) that gas molecules alone do not exhibit either pressure or the transmission of sound. However, the simple act of putting a large number of gas molecules together in a container gives rise to entirely distinct and unsuspected new properties, pressure and sound. The new properties require unique rules, the details of description of individual atoms or molecules being inadequate to model the novel behaviors emerging on a higher plane of abstraction.

To state a hypothesis, the brain is a system endowed with a unique structure and an environment, not only a composition. And the structure of the brain includes the highly organized connections of its constituent neurons, creating untold intricate neural networks of momentous consequence. The result is a system, or more precisely, a complex intertwining of innumerable, functionally interacting subsystems, that produce the emerging property of mind. The mind perceives, thinks, wills and carries out many other functions, properties totally absent from the repertoire of individual neuron function. And yet, it is such neuron function, and only that activity, that creates the process we call mind.

The latter hypothesis, in and of itself, that mind is an emerging property of brain activity, does not prove the point. However, as discussed in Chapter 5, there is not one shred of credible evidence that mind cannot be completely explained in terms of brain activity. The overwhelming scientific consensus and the point of view of the present book is that the mind is totally an emerging property related to brain complexity, structure (pattern of interconnection), and action.

The Mystifying Binding Problem

It will be recalled that the last two chapters showed our perceptions to be reassembled from elemental features extracted in multiple, parallel brain paths. Importantly, for any one perception, the specific paths and even sub-elements thereof are unique and, in most cases, widely distributed physically in the brain. Yet, in spite of great physical distinction and dispersion, these multiple, parallel, pre-perceptual processes must also be subsequently reunited, the diverse processing threads of necessity being pulled together to permit unified thought. Obviously, if the above scheme really represents perceptual function, the system requires some 'glue' to interject order and coordination into otherwise independent parallel processing. The search for the linking mechanism of perceptual processing, the glue, has been termed the binding problem.

How might the binding system work? One innovative line of pursuit involves rule-based computer models of human cognition. The first rule-based computer models of cognitive activity were initiated by Allen Newell and Herbert Simon in the late 1960s. But it is instructive to examine a specific example of much more recent vintage, a computer model devised by John Holland termed an adaptive agent. While other lines of study exist, elements of Holland's work are particularly convergent with the theme and content of present discussion. A much more in-depth summary of Holland's studies can be found in the book *Complexity (Chapter 5)* by Mitchell Waldrop. Holland's purpose was to develop a process that uniquely combined certain aspects of consciousness. I have taken the liberty of extending Holland's concept to include the subconscious mind as well, since this appears to be a natural extension.

The key to Holland's adaptive agent (which exhibits similarities at least in part to a cortical column or to a skill unit!) is a metaphor of a bulletin board in the mind. Of course, the bulletin board is meant to represent a function, but no actual physical bulletin board residing in the mind is suggested. In fact, almost certainly any such bulletin board function would be physically widely dispersed, since no localization of this function has been detected in the brain.

In any case, a central store, the bulletin board, is modeled as a clearinghouse for data transfer and processing. Individual adaptive agents each represent a particular rule or a specialist in processing one type of data. The system runs in cycles. At the beginning of a new cycle, the clearinghouse displays messages from all relevant adaptive agents from the last cycle. Each adaptive agent reviews its own specialized repertoire, looks to see if any related postings occurred in the central store, and if a subject match is found, the adaptive agent sends updated information to the clearinghouse. Thus the clearinghouse system provides a focal point for information interaction. The clearinghouse is also envisioned as capable of receiving outside information from environmental detectors (sensors) and to be capable of acting on the environment through effectors.

Holland built several novel features into his ultimate model. First, it was felt essential to avoid using symbols. The use of symbols had been common practice for decades in computer modeling of intelligent processes, but Holland wished to strictly employ binary code (to best mimic brain groups either firing or not). Second, also contrary to prior technique elsewhere, the individual adaptive agents were not given instructions ahead of time — Holland designed the system so that each agent learned its specialty and the rules of engagement from scratch. Third, conventional wisdom had also been to use some form of centralized control, but Holland elected to let each adaptive agent fight it out for supremacy. The latter environment was implemented using an innovative scheme where adaptive agents essentially bid for recognition. Each adaptive agent was rewarded or penalized over time (many successive system cycles) depending upon relative success or failure, as measured by feedback from the environment (the system learned by experience).

The result was that, on average, system behavior converged on strategies that were relatively successful. However, a degree of behavioral spontaneity was also manifest, and mistakes had positive value in providing data relative to defining less fruitful approaches that further enriched accumulated experience and enhanced learning. Finally, Holland incorporated an element called a genetic algorithm. The latter protocol provided a means for the system to occasionally explore new reaction strategies in random fashion, as opposed to being perpetually locked into old learned routines.

The full implementation of Holland's approach took several years. Then, over a number of additional years, Holland's general method was tested in various situations by several independent researchers. Some of the test situations included playing poker, running simulated mazes, simple robotic controllers, and more. But the most dramatic test during this era (the early 1980s) was an elaborate controller for a simulated gas pipeline designed by one of Holland's students, David Goldberg. At the time, it was far and away the most complex task that a Holland-like computer model had tackled, having the goal of achieving throughput demands optimized for operational economy in a system with hundreds of gas compressors and hundreds of miles of pipe, in the face of sporadic leaks and constantly changing customer demands, while perpetually maintaining flow parameters within safety limits. In the modeled pipeline system, all of the important parameters interacted, and the problem was basically intractable using conventional mathematical analysis. Yet, Goldberg's Holland-like computer simulation exhibited sterling performance.

The importance of the pipeline archetype for our present purposes is the demonstration of a system with internal bargaining and competition. More specifically, a self-learning system composed of competing elements that were required to arbitrate for a role in system output, using a structure plausible for gross relationships in the brain, performed in a manner reminiscent of consciousness and multiple-mindlet management as developed in earlier chapters.

Holland's approach involved hypothetical adaptive agents that remind one of cortical columns or skill units in many ways. But it is interesting that the same concept could apply, in principle, to ensembles of cortical and general brain functional groups as well, including, in the terminology of the present volume, individual mindlets. Thus, the paradoxical notion of the overall, unified mind, operating through multiple individual mindlets competing for control in the absence of an ultimate governor, is seen to have real functional potentiality. Of course, the described work is from only a tiny niche of studies ongoing in the fascinating field of artificial intelligence, about which we will have more to say later in the present chapter.

Several binding hypotheses currently populate the neuroscience community. Of the more prominent, one involves entrainment of activity in separated brain centers by mutual interaction, and another proposes wide distribution of a central synchronizing signal train. Others feel that phenomena such as lockstep or at least synchronous firing are too close to the level of individual neural behavior to be likely of success. The latter viewpoint argues that the search may be more profitable if the simultaneous behavior of significant, separated groups of neurons are examined. It may even be necessary to use chaos theory in an attempt to extract real information content from seemingly random firing of distributed neurons. It is too early in the course of binding problem studies to hazard a forceful prediction. However, my personal intuition is that the answer will lean toward the latter suggestion, involving, at least in part, statistically (collectively) coordinated processing within widely distributed neuronal groups that is, though, not characterized by individual neuron synchronization dictated by some central pacemaker.

The Hardware and Software of Mind

The subject of hardware and software is important for later discussion. It is therefore useful to lay some foundation relative to terminology and inter-relationships. The terms hardware and software usually induce the image of computers. However, hardware and software are employed here in a much broader sense. For example, we mentioned previously how the brain and the mind are analogous in some ways to hardware and software, respectively. That being said, however, the current discussion begins in the context of computers before returning to the mind and the mind-body problem.

In the language of computers, the term hardware designates actual physical machinery. Hardware is composed of such elements as circuit boards, integrated circuits, hard drives, storage media, and so forth. The hardware label also includes the complete description of how the various hardware elements are configured and connected.

Software, in turn, denotes computer programs that can be 'run' on the hardware. In other words, computer software represents a codified, step-by-step specification for carrying out a process within computer hardware, usually acting on external input data to render some transformed output information or action. The series of instructions that constitute software are always stored in some medium. As one example, hard disks and floppy disks represent means to permanently store encrypted information for personal computers. As a second illustration, personal computers typically employ special computer chips (e.g., random access memory) to provide what is termed working memory when the hardware and software are in use (when the program is running).

Around mid-century, Alan Turing derived a splendid proof that, given a sufficient level of complication and flexibility, any computing machine is equivalent to any other. The computing devices might operate at entirely different speeds, and the availability of adequate memory must be provided. But given such leveling of the playing field, a program properly prepared for any suitable machine would always produce the same output when fed identical inputs.

It can therefore be shown that the hardware is not really very important, because the software can be run on any computer that meets some minimal standards. Taken to the extreme, in fact, some have argued that the hardware is irrelevant, and it is the software alone (the series of instructions; the algorithm; the program) that represents the real essence of the process. This is the position of what has been termed the strong artificial intelligence view (discussed in more detail later).

Our goal here is to explore mind as it relates to the broad issue of hardware versus software. This is not at all a discussion of whether the brain is a computer — that topic is addressed later. Here we focus on just what type of system is required to undergo thought.

There are some fascinating ramifications of the idea that software is everything. Insight can be gained through the teleportation concept familiar from science fiction. In a popular version, an individual is somehow subjected to a whole-body imaging (documentation) process sufficient for the person to be disassembled, electromagnetically transported (beamed) to a new location, and then reassembled. Use of beamed electromagnetic radiation (or some other, presently unknown, rapid communications medium) is critical. It is not the actual matter of the traveler that is supposedly transported, because an electromagnetic beam transmits information, not substance. What is purportedly transported is all of the information necessary to recreate at the destination, from new matter, an exact copy of the original person.

This all seems straightforward enough. But let's delve deeper. Teleportation also implies that the traveler's memories, feelings, subconscious processes and everything else, absolutely everything else, synchronized at some exact instant of time to retain proper temporal relationships, is dutifully duplicated in perfect detail. The problem is vastly more arduous than, say, recreating every atom of the entire material body, in every detail, although of course that is a given. A far bigger challenge is to regenerate the exact state of every structural and functional component of the body and brain relative to interactions with other components. For instance, such a result would require, in part, exactly recreating for every relevant molecule in the body and brain all atomic and molecular energy states, inter-atomic and inter-molecular bonds and other associations critical to ongoing interactions, processes and potentialities. Otherwise, countless elements of the mind and body would not be restored to their instantaneous, pre-transport functional states at the destination teleport.

So let's say, in a thought experiment, that you are teleported from one point to a distant location, for example, the moon. Some intriguing questions arise. Is the resultant mind on the moon the same mind — in other words, is that really you on the moon, with your old conscious awareness, self, and everything else intact? If so, then the essence of the mind really does seem to be the software, because none of the old hardware survived the trip, not one atom. Would you really be willing to submit to teleportation yourself, knowing that none of your corporeal substance would be the same?

Let's add another perplexing complication to our thought experiment. Let's impose a satellite relay for the electromagnetic beam midway between the earth and the moon. We presume that the satellite receives the signal from earth, stores the information for some time, and then later retransmits the data to the moon. Upon receipt of the data from earth, the storage system on board the satellite has all of the information necessary to reconstruct you, including your mind. Assuming suitable hardware was available to compile and 'run' your program, you and your mind could in fact be created, and, moreover, duplicated many times. Lets imagine further that the hardware running the program was not a recreation of your body but rather some form of non-living (according to parochial earth standards) machine. By running the proper segments of your program to recreate only the functions of your mind, would you and your unique self and conscious awareness suddenly become manifest with a machine as the gantry for the mind and body?

These seemingly outlandish thoughts are presented to expand perspective on the mind-body problem. Concrete consensus is not yet available, but we will see the development and interpretation of related thoughts in the next two sections.

Artificial Intelligence

An inspiring area of endeavor in recent years has been the field of artificial intelligence. The goals of artificial intelligence are to design machines that accomplish and eventually exceed the equivalent of human mentation. There are at least four areas of endeavor within artificial intelligence:

Robotics — The design of controlled mechanical systems that can perform processes requiring some intelligence and that previously were dependent totally on human conduct; the goal is to achieve levels of performance superior to human capabilities;

Expert Systems — The coding of a body of knowledge and skills, ranging from a specific activity to, say, an entire profession, so that the machine-like system could take the place of experienced humans in actual practice; ultimately, extensive and adaptable intelligent decision making is the goal;

Psychology — Systems that mimic the behavior of the human brain are developed, in the hope that both successes and failures will illuminate aspects of human actions and interactions; and

Mind — Modeling of processes that accomplish analysis and decision making, using architectures both similar to and distinct from known brain relationships, are employed to provide insight on how the mind works and to advance general understanding of mechanized thinking machines.

Virtually all of the current work is heavily dependent on computers. However, in the broad sense, any means to accomplish the task is fair game for artificial intelligence.

Since inception in the 1950s, the field of artificial intelligence has made notable progress. Interestingly, however, the advancements have come much slower than originally thought. In the beginning, practitioners felt that machines with high-level thought would have been realized before now. Bold early predictions included the rapid coming of systems that would recognize objects, control intelligent robots, understand stories, comprehend speech, invent systems and theories, and many other human-like capabilities.

In actuality, though, even today, there is still a long way to go to achieve the lofty early goals of advanced machine cognition. Nevertheless, a strong consensus still remains that the objective can really be accomplished, and no evidence exists suggesting that any known brain action cannot be programmed. The latter interpretation is intended to include recognized types of motivations, such as emotion, aggression, curiosity, hunger, and other classes of sensory-analysis-action schemes that may complicate ordinary performance. It is just that the provocative work to bring intelligent programs and machines to the human level has proved more difficult and prolonged than originally expected.

But although short of the ultimate goal, artificial intelligence has achieved impressive results. First, prevalence of robotics in industry is increasing rapidly, even if the average level of intelligence employed is relatively low. Second, thousands of expert systems have entered the commercial realm, carrying out such surrogate tasks as monitoring assembly lines or conducting manufacturing quality control, sorting bank checks, translating text from one language to another, pattern recognition, educational and training programs, and others far too numerous to mention. Third, psychologically oriented studies are proceeding on two synergistic fronts: a) a top-down philosophy, looking at intelligent actions formulated as intact, interacting subsystems, featuring such things as central decision-making and world maps, and the ability to deal with abstract concepts without regard to lower-level subcomponents; and b) a bottom-up ideology, where individual mindless actions are combined in unique ways to create emerging purposeful behavior (e.g., the discussion of Marvin Minsky's work near the end of Chapter 2). Finally, investigations in the mind-like subdivision of artificial intelligence are largely focusing on special structural substrates such as neural networks, and strategies and algorithms that provide insight related to decision making, dealing with abstract concepts, and thinking activities.

Is The Mind a Computer?

The whole premise of artificial intelligence is that thinking machines are not only possible but realistic. Artificial intelligence defines its prime objective to be the development of intelligent machines that can out perform human cognition relative to any selected task.

To date, humans still reign supreme on earth. But are we on top if the entire universe is surveyed? Currently, we don't know. For what it's worth, my money is on the universe for two reasons. First, as discussed in Chapter 4, life probably exists elsewhere in the galaxy and also in the universe beyond. For that reason, given the extremely short span of truly human intellect compared to the age of the universe, we are in fact likely the youngest (and therefore probably the least developed) intelligence in our own Milky Way galaxy. But second, and more to the point here, beings with superior intelligence residing elsewhere have probably already designed thinking machines that far exceed human capabilities. The development of intelligent machines may have been proceeding for billions of years somewhere in the universe at large, and even within our younger Milky Way galaxy.

From our earthly point of view, computers are currently the only serious contenders to human cognition. And at today's stage of development, computers fall far short of humans in the thinking department. True, computers have, for example, been programmed to play chess at the grand master level, and IBM's supercomputer and program named Deep Thought just (Spring, 1997) beat world champion Gary Kasperov in a six game match. But the details of even the most proficient of contemporary chess programs do not really operate through intuitive reasoning so much as by way of massive, brute-force, high-speed, probabilistic examination of alternative moves. Nevertheless, as our look at the field of artificial intelligence showed, the capacity for machines to operate along lines reminiscent of human thinking is growing rapidly. And the mind-versus-computer gap has less to do with hardware than software — the biggest hurdle is that we haven't yet learned how to write software programs with high levels of reasoning and intuition.

Another issue also lurks. What do we mean when we talk about a thinking machine? Put another way, how should we compare a person to a machine? The most direct comparison would be to define a standard test that adequately differentiates cognition from non-cognitive processing. Then, at any point in time, an experiment could be conducted to compare capabilities. But even if we reach a point (which I believe is inevitable, within a few decades) where a computer matches or exceeds human performance in one or more areas, is that enough to endow the computer with cognition? What about sensations and emotions? What about conscious awareness and the flowing sense of time?

We can only infer the existence of other minds. I assume other people have minds because they act as if they do. I know about one mind, mine, through a lifetime of introspection. I see other humans behaving in a fashion very similar to me in untold situations, and I presume by analogy they must also have a mind. Higher animals also appear to have minds, although apparently not as developed as humans. If I were to judge a machine, say, a computer, relative to cognitive ability, I should make judgments based only on performance (behavior), to keep the playing field level. If a computer (or any other non-living machine) were designed to respond in a fashion identical to that of a person relative to every conceivable outside influence (including tests to detect consciousness), there would be no basis to avoid assigning consciousness and the ability of thinking to the system.

Reviewed below are three primary arguments typically employed to dispute the notion that computers (or any kind of mechanism) could ever think, even in principle. Each is analyzed in some detail. Also discussed is an additional factor related to human emotion.

Rigid Logic. The creed here is that the computer is purely mechanical, automatic and mindless in action, and therefore can achieve only what has been empowered through programming. Computers are said to be totally incapable of motivation, emotional sensation, compassion and other human qualities, due to a foundation in the rigid rule-based operation of discrete components (transistors, diodes, etc.). This line of defense just does not coincide with the preponderance of evidence. First, the brain is also discrete at the component level, being a mass of singular brain cells interconnected in a highly organized fashion, each cell mindlessly functioning according to local physics. And yet, by definition, the brain (mind) is certainly capable of generating human-like behavior. Second, even with the present embryonic state of artificial intelligence, computer programs have been written that demonstrate intelligence, spontaneity, and other primary properties of human conduct, at least to some degree. Alternatively, in the currently burgeoning field of neural networks, using computer or hardware based circuits that learn through experience purely by virtue of real-time component interactions (without running a step-by-step program), human-like processes have been repeatedly demonstrated.

A careful examination shows that all of the qualities typically called upon to defend the uniqueness of humans are not so mysterious after all. Such notions are relics of a past where today's tremendous computers and knowledge were unknown and unsuspected. Contemporary advancements have completely reversed the consensus of workers in the brain sciences, the scientific nay sayers being primarily from outside of brain research. But the results have not yet percolated down to the average person.

At present, the neurophysiological data does not reveal any brain or mind activity that, in principle, does not appear directly amenable to programming. For example, a peak at motivation and emotion is instructive. At the most basic level, motivation can be viewed from one perspective as changing the relative priorities of certain goals, and goals can be viewed as set points in feedback control systems. In turn, emotional reactions can be modeled physiologically in roughly the same way, differing largely in degree. For instance, emotional reactions can be characterized as the resetting of priorities in sensory, motor, and higher mental functions to particularly heightened and highly reactive (or, alternatively, suppressed or constrained), but otherwise normal, states. The altered state of emotional charge may also, depending on the nature and intensity of the stimulus and/or reaction, add or remove select response patterns to or from the original mix. But again, there is no reason to invoke any special, mystical mechanisms or agents. Emotional responses and accompanying conscious experiences can be modeled as modified states of normal physiology.

An additional example may be helpful. In the early days of artificial intelligence, W. Grey Walter built a mechanized, computer-controlled 'tortoise' that roamed the rooms and hallways of a research building in a usually carefree fashion. However, when the batteries in the tortoise began to run low, tortoise behavior was programmed to change, adopting a mode that actively hunted electrical wall sockets. When a socket was found, the device roboticly connected to the socket and recharged its batteries. Then, once the batteries were charged, the tortoise would resume its previous exploratory wanderings. Especially if some 'emotional' reactions (e.g., impatient-like elevated sensitivity to stimuli; quicker but also rougher [nervous] responsiveness; more aggressive tactics of engagement with encountered objects; heightened attention to outside events; etc.) had been included in the program as well, in a fashion designed to mimic appropriate additional human and animal behaviors, this simple process could be made to exhibit any and all of the salient emotional earmarks of motivated human hunger and feeding.

Religious Teachings. The religious arguments against thinking computers take the form of claiming life is endowed with some animating vital force not present in non-living material, and in the related assertion that machines can have no soul. Each issue is addressed in turn below.

Regarding some unique vital ingredient for life, as developed in Chapter 4, there just is not a shred of scientific evidence to suggest that any ghostly essence is associated in the slightest way with living material. Life has been found to be an extremely complex, hierarchically-structured, self-organized form of normal matter, majestic and stupendous in breadth and depth, and bursting with emerging properties, but nothing more.

As far as the soul is concerned, the concept has essentially dissolved from common usage in recent decades, and is now basically relegated to religious circles. In a functional sense, the definition of soul seems to equate to the word mind as used in the present book. But typical teachings have also pictured the soul as an element that is immaterial and yet is still a substance, the stuff that makes up thoughts, some mystical disembodied thing free of physical law that forms the counterpart of the body. This is the dualist theory of the mind (soul) developed to a fine pitch by the 17th century philosopher Descartes. The dualist viewpoint has been widely incorporated into Christian faith, and also seems still to best approximate the belief of the masses.

It can be shown that the idea of the soul, though, is vague and contradictory. Talk of the soul is couched in ambiguous language, being a substance (thing) on one hand but in turn not exhibiting properties associated with ordinary matter (e.g., composition, size, weight, position in space) or reverence to natural law. In other words, the soul is undetectable, and so the soul's existence is declared by pure assertion to be beyond study. Yet the soul is said to provide the main seat of self and of consciousness, through some mysterious coupling mechanism, in a seamless fashion that blends continuously and perfectly with tangible brain and bodily function.

One can always argue that just because a vital force in life or a governing soul has not yet been detected, that one or both may still exist. This position is true on the surface, but does not represent productive reasoning. Arguably the greatest piece of wisdom humans have learned from science is that advances in knowledge have followed from requiring hypotheses to be testable and for theories to be proven and reproducible, always to the limits of current knowledge. The notions of an intangible vital force and of the soul are non-testable by definition, undermine the entire edifice of the scientific method, and are empty and counterproductive. Until proven different, the emotional attachment of some people to such sterile defiance of known facts and rational investigation seems utterly without merit.

The Non-Digital Brain. Another line of reasoning occasionally employed to argue against a brain-computer similarity is the fact that the brain is not digital in nature. This argument centers on the fact that common computers are digital in approach, whereas neurons do not behave like all-or-nothing (digital; either on or off) devices. This view is dissected below.

In general, it is true that neurons do not usually fire in response to a single incoming impulse from another neuron, but more typically require many reasonably concurrent inputs, often hundreds or thousands. Thus the neuron is really what would be described technically as an analog device, not digital, responding in an integrating fashion to the relative timing and strength of collective inputs.

The only sense in which a neuron might be considered digital is in terms of its own firing (generation of one or more nerve impulses). All of the inputs to a given neuron contribute (variably, depending on 'importance') to alter the cell membrane potential of the main cell body and especially the beginning zone (hillock) of the single output process, the axon. If the membrane potential of the axon hillock changes sufficiently, the cell fires an impulse. A neuron impulse is a propagating electrical disturbance that travels down the axon somewhat like the burning locus of a fuse for an explosive. In addition, the neuron usually keeps firing repetitively as long as the axon hillock membrane potential dictates. If the axon hillock membrane potential does not change sufficiently, the cell does not fire. Thus, cell firing is controlled by a threshold phenomenon in the axon hillock membrane. This is the only sense in which neuron behavior can be considered digital. But the real nature of neuron network functioning is much more akin to analog performance, due to: a) the general requirements for large numbers of inputs to 'turn on' individual neurons; and b) the fact that physiological networks of neurons exhibit much redundancy (parallel processing) and therefore tend to function statistically.

In any case, so the brain isn't digital — so what? The brain is certainly a computer, because it is a biological computation machine. All of the neurophysiological functions that have been identified in diverse brain structures appear to be computations, processing data (encrypted as neural activity) in terms of pathway structure (arrangement of neurons) and the patterns (duration and frequency) of neural impulse trains (see in particular P.M. Churchland, *A Neuro-computational Perspective*). Furthermore, other types of computing machines exist in addition to simple digital machines such as common personal computers (PCs). Three examples are particularly relevant. Analog computers function by developing dynamic, continuously varying interrelationships to compute the time course of interacting parameters involved in ongoing processes. In turn, artificial neural networks, as described earlier, function in real time by virtue of the interconnections of dynamic components, learning through guided experience (training) to accomplish useful functions. Finally, parallel computers, devices that break a process into multiple pathways and then concurrently carry out individual path computations to greatly accelerate processing, are enjoying an explosive growth of commercial and scientific applications.

Today's parallel processors are almost all digital, but parallel analog machines are certainly feasible. Depending on the subsystem, the brain shows dramatic use of analog, parallel, and digital data processing. In addition, the brain certainly employs neural network-like processing almost by definition, since the whole concept of artificial neural networks was developed on a simplified model of neuronal function. Obviously, the contention that the brain is not like a digital computer contains some superficial truth, but fails as an argument against drawing strong analogies between computers (machines or anything else that carry out computation) and the brain (which is an organic computing machine).

Emotion. One of the problems with the human condition relates to an issue discussed previously, the overpowering propensity for our minds to fill in missing detail. The mind seems to have a compelling need for complete explanations, apparently to efficiently organize and navigate the world with the form of mind we are given. We also regularly contaminate our consciousness and memories with emotional associations and reactions.

We are constantly subjected to situations where our information is incomplete and where emotions are a part of conscious experience. But our minds incorporate emotional overtones and fill in the gaps with educated guesses, seemingly to create representations of the present and past that meet some inner requirement for internal consistency and completeness. It would appear that this strategy served the ancestors of our modern mind well, given how ingrained the behavior is at present. But humankind has recently ascended from mythic and even more primordial minds, to enter the realm of abstract reasoning where meticulous accuracy and precision are paramount. We have not been truly thinking very long, in an evolutionary sense, and we are not very good at high level reasoning. For this reason, constant diligence must be exercised to actively avoid the natural tendency to uncritically smooth the mental landscape and to spice our consciousness and memories with emotion.

Reflex reactions against artificial intelligence and the thought of the mind being like a computer are areas where emotions run rampant. As an example, a small number of renowned scientists (mostly from disciplines outside of the neurosciences) have declared that the study of consciousness is a waste of time — that the basis and details of consciousness are unknowable. I would argue that this is a bizarre and misguided point of view. The true nature of consciousness is not yet known. The belief that pervaded (and caused!) the Dark Ages was that nothing could be learned through inquiry and analysis. Activism by scientists proclaiming the futility of studying consciousness is worse than useless, it is unhealthy and harmful. Furthermore, it is totally inconsistent with the mind-boggling success of the scientific approach throughout recent centuries, and especially in the 1900s.

Solution to the Mind-Body Problem

The mind-body problem arose out of the dualist viewpoint, that mind and body (brain) are two distinct materials. Dialog earlier in this chapter showed that dualism, in all of the many forms which have surfaced, is not acceptable because it is not consistent with known facts. But there is another dimension to the mind-body problem that historically has been generally overlooked.

To understand the mind-body problem, the most essential fact is to realize that direct comparisons of mind and body are irrelevant. The real crux of the problem is that both entities, the mind and the body (brain), descriptively inhabit different levels of abstraction. Direct comparisons or contrasts don't work because there are no common elements for focus. Thus, any attempt at a feature-by-feature correlation is meaningless. For comparison, how could we compare the properties of a language (information content, grammar, spelling, etc.) to the design features of the individual symbols (letters, numbers, etc.) that embody the language in written form? We can't, because such comparisons don't even make sense. Written language and lettering occur on two entirely different levels of abstraction, and follow distinct laws (rules).

Other examples of the abstraction dilemma can be cited, such as comparing:
a) the socialized structure of an ant or bee colony to the behavior of an isolated ant or bee;
b) the properties of individual electronic components to the behavior of a television set;
c) the characteristics of individual ingredients to a soufflé; and
d) countless others.

It is much easier to analyze the latter examples, because we are emotionally detached. We don't so easily fall in the trap of an abstraction dilemma when dealing with items and systems to which we are introspectively indifferent.

But in confronting the mind, Western culture has for centuries steadfastly permeated our language and indoctrinated our world view with dualist concepts. Additionally, we experience often potent emotional reactions when such deeply embedded convictions are even mildly threatened. But by being dutifully objective, and dissecting the mind-body problem within the context of the abstraction dilemma, we can suddenly see that there really isn't a problem at all.

As shown in prior discussion, neither the mind nor the brain are as yet completely understood. An understanding of both the mind and brain remain paramount problems in their own right, and are probably pivotal to progress regarding many other major problems as well. Furthermore, we need to learn the details of how particular brain activity correlates with each aspect of the mind. Nevertheless, all of the voluminous neurophysiological evidence suggests that the mind is an emerging property of the brain, and nothing more. In my thinking, the traditional mind-body problem has been recently recognized as purely an abstraction dilemma, and has therefore been resolved.

In summary, as we come to the end of Part II, we have developed a point of view regarding life, consciousness, and the unique advanced awareness displayed by humans designated here as self-consciousness. The developed theme reveals a majestic self-aware mind that is solely the result of emerging properties of the self-organized brain. This provides, within the context of the present interpretation, the short answer to Central Question [2] identified in Chapter One, "What is the Nature and Make-Up of Mind?" A more detailed answer, integrated with responses for all of the other Central Questions of this book are presented in Chapter 10 (at the end of Part III).

Assuming that the latter view, the consensus of practicing neuroscientists, stands the test of time, the ramifications shake the very foundation of perceived existence. We would find ourselves in a universe that began from a gargantuan cloud of seemingly very simple constituents, but one somehow inherently endowed with the potential to self-create systems like the human brain and its attendant self-consciousness. Thus, the primordial cloud is envisioned as evolving to eventually contemplate itself. And who can say where the ultimate limits of advancing complexity lie, if in fact there are any limits.

Yet the universe and our role therein is far from clear. We have much to learn. Also, our thinking about existence is complicated by conflicting dogma from religion, science, and personal thoughts and desires. Under such tumultuous circumstances, the result of our incomplete state of knowledge, what can we say about the best pathway to god and an understanding of the universe and our existence? It is to the latter conundrum, the subject of Part III, that the discussion now shifts.

PART III

God, Purpose, and Existence

PART III

God, Purpose and Existence

The objective of Part III is to pull together the developments of Parts I and II, and to bring to bear new data and ideas, to provide the best current answers to the six Central Questions posed in Chapter 1. The last four of the six Central Questions, Questions 3-6, were not addressed in any great detail in Parts I and II, or were not treated at all.

The first chapter of Part III, Chapter 8, is directed largely to a lurking side issue, monumental and compelling in form and substance. All of the six Central Questions (see Chapter 1) addressed by this book are questions with huge religious overtones. So how does religion relate to the scientific concepts being presently discussed, and how can the religious and scientific points of view be reconciled? That is the focus of Chapter 8, which also introduces important and perhaps startling potential ideas about the nature of god.

Next, Chapter 9 integrates previous discussion and new facts to highlight the apparent central role of consciousness in the universe. The physics of the universe, self-organized complexity, life, and the remarkable implications conveyed by the actual presence of intelligent life are used to analyze the traditional concept of god, and how we might view our interface with the ultimate organizing influence of the universe. The treatment also peeks at a remarkable new holism recently discovered to pervade the universe. This discovery, in a shocking way, violates all common sense, and fuels the mystery and elegance of our self-evolving world.

Finally, Chapter 10 develops the notion that the leading edge of the sensational self-organized complexity of the universe is consciousness, and a reinforcement of the concept that the cosmos can be purposeful and yet not preordained. Then, a different approach, a top-down analysis of ideas presented throughout the book is used to develop one example of a model universe. More importantly, the process of actual model construction is outlined, to provide a means for the non-expert to build his or her own model, based on their own personal beliefs. Finally, the six Central Questions of the book, developed in Chapter 1, are each addressed in turn to provide, through a final synthesis, a brief summary of known data and present interpretation.

Chapter 8
Religion versus Science

The Two Great Systems of Thought

By far the greatest system of human thought throughout history has been religion. Collectively, the diverse religions of the world cast a principal and often dominant influence over the individual actions and lives of the average person. True, there are tremendous differences between religions, and culture-by-culture dissimilarities are often evident in the interpretation and practice of any given religion as well. But here the view is focused on religions as a group, especially those of Western persuasion. And overall, such religions have exerted widespread leverage and control over our mental and physical lives in the past, and still do today.

Yet, compared to holy teachings, spiritual practice is found to be an enigma. First, most governments have no religious ties or at most, a loose association with a particular faith. The Vatican, Israel and Ireland are exceptions, being legally cast as religious states. The recent resurgence of Islamic fundamentalism in the Arab world is also noteworthy due to widespread influence, and other examples could be cited. But, in general, states typically are, at least officially, non-religious. Second, the organization and conduct of non-governmental institutions, private businesses, and personal interactions typically show little connection with religious teachings and, in fact, often contrast with stipulated behavioral dictums. Especially in the Western world and modernized areas elsewhere, many people with religious persuasion live two lives. One is an internalized activity revolving around a personal faith and world view. But, paradoxically, a dissimilar public persona is often exhibited in the conduct of daily affairs that is more indifferent, utilitarian and selfish.

Turning to science, people find that the latter system of thought has grown immensely in impact through recent times, a trend that seems destined to continue in the foreseeable future. Science profoundly effects virtually everyone in the world, the faithful, indifferent and agnostic alike, in one way or another. Prolific trappings and other evidence of science exists everywhere we turn and at every level of description. Science has forever transformed the aboriginal existence from which we sprang into the rapidly evolving throes of contemporary society.

But an intriguing pattern has emerged. Focusing on the industrialized world, the population and intensity of religious attendance has gone down in rough step with the rising impact of science. But the latter phenomenon seems not to be due to people switching worship loyalty from religion to science. In fact, the common person shows surprising ignorance regarding natural law, technology, and the immense impact of science on our lives and especially our perspective on existence. So where has the world view of the average person gone? It seems to have remained basically religious, but has become more internalized. Adherence to systematized ritual has declined, but people's world view based on divine control and intervention has remained relatively unchanged. And so the fact that science has become the dominant force in influencing our lives and environment places us in the strange (and probably transitional) state where we are internally religious but externally pragmatic.

There is perhaps at least one partial explanation of the encroachment of science into our general behavior. The impact of science has progressively risen to the point that, especially in recent decades, the urgency of constant religious support has been greatly diminished. People just don't need or use religion as much any more to deal with the trials and tribulations of the modern world. One reason is that issues formerly limited to strictly religious attention (e.g., understanding of morality, family, health, existence, etc.) have been increasingly transcended by advancing science.

So we find that science has come to address more and more of the issues previously restricted to the religious province. And the process has revealed that much of the religious teachings just don't square with the facts. However, the disciplines of science and of education have not done an effective job in disseminating the revelations that scientific study has wrought. The public remains largely unaware of the incredible physical infrastructure of life and the universe, and the portentous insight to our existence that science has uncovered. As we saw, science has come to control much outward behavior. But deep within, our inner beliefs, our personal feelings about existence and our place in the world, have remained largely unchanged from centuries past.

Importantly, there is not the need for an either-or choice between religion and science. Those individuals with religious persuasions could adopt a modified spiritual construct, integrating fundamental moral dictums with the compelling contributions to understanding that science offers and portends. And to survive, religions and religious authorities will most likely need to accept and actually begin to promote current fact, stand ready to adapt to future scientific developments which are sure to come, and be honest with the average person.

The present chapter examines both religion and science, how these omnipresent systems of thought interrelate, and some key implications relative to human pondering of existence. It is therefore essential that science and religion be carefully defined and described to facilitate meaningful dialog. The next two sections are directed to the latter end.

What Is Science?

We have come to enjoy a certain level of understanding about the world in which we live. But the road to progress has not been an easy one. Research has shown that the earliest human minds were strongly shaped for the most part by happenings that were strange and unexpected, not by mundane, ordinary events. Unusual events such as floods, severe weather, and other natural phenomena caught people's attention and came to be incorporated into folklore. The mind had also achieved a complexity that apparently began to demand descriptive reasons for natural occurrences. Thus, legends, ritual and other behavioral patterns arose to provide mystical and spiritual explanations for processes that, at the time, could not otherwise be explained.

To aid discussion, three periods of human development will be identified, aboriginal, religious and scientific. In the first or aboriginal phase, beginning at least 50,000 years ago in the era of the early mythic mind (see the discussion of Chapter 6), the world view of primordial humans has been found to be one controlled by mysterious, largely invisible external forces. Religious thought began under such conditions, but was weakly organized in step with the aboriginal nature of the small human groups typical of the times. Much later, humankind is seen to have evolved to embrace a second world view, what we are calling here the religious phase. The religious era would have been well underway 10,000 years ago, during late stages of the mythic mind period. During these times, religion has been seen to progressively take a much more dominant and eventually commanding stance in the daily lives of individuals and in the organization of societies.

Late in the religious phase (in the era of the mythic-to-theoretic mind transition; see Chapter 6), humans have been found to be witness to and participants in the emergence of the great religions. Finally, in the scientific era, which began about four hundred years ago and within which we now reside, humankind is seen to enter a modern period where science began to progressively displace religion. So far during the scientific era, science has already reached a position of overwhelming influence on our daily lives, having surpassed religion in that regard certainly no later than some point in the current century. But paradoxically, the world view of the average person is found to have remained much more religious than scientific.

Religious phase maturity was found to be fostered by a mounting realization. For the early mythic mind, when religious thought began, most of experience seemed due to extraordinary events, and so virtually all of life was associated with external deities and influences. Later, late-stage mythics apparently discovered the fact, very obvious to us now, that the phenomenal events which dictated earlier thought were really infrequent aberrations appearing on a pervasive ongoing sea of ordinary causality. As this realization matured, the whole perception of the world was found to have changed. During this beginning of the religious phase, the mystical view of the aboriginal era was gradually displaced by acceptance of ordinary, relatively uneventful nature as the norm. Such thinking had become thoroughly entrenched in Western thought well before the Dark Ages. Most of experience was considered ordinary, and only occasional events were given religious significance. But constant religious diligence throughout daily life was still felt necessary to stave off or minimize problems if and when they did occur. In the latter fashion, the Western world had an entrenched religious world view coming into the technical revolutions of the scientific phase.

During the religious era, ordinary nature was characterized by predictability. Given well behaved circumstances, events followed a cause-and-effect pattern and therefore were reasonably predictable. Ordinary nature had come to be accepted as a given, really without much but a religious explanation for being. In contrast, extraordinary events and the topic of existence itself had become singled out as needing explanation. The realization that ordinary nature had major significance was an essential prerequisite to further insight, but in and of itself was an incomplete and unsatisfactory world view. The emergence of science provided both the focus and the basis to explain the ordinary as well as the extraordinary.

The reorientation of knowledge accompanying the emergence of science has been shown to be nothing short of spectacular. The emergence was spread over a considerable period of time. Recall that the birth of true science has been placed for present discussion several hundred years ago as the Dark Ages came to a close. But elements of the overall emergence of the concept of a dependable, reliable nature had occurred over thousands of years, beginning certainly as early as the growth and flourishing of Greek civilization. The key ingredients have been characterized as the process and mind-set of describing and documenting the world, and the development of abbreviations and symbols to permit the abstraction and manipulation of concepts independent of raw information. Science is a system of thought dedicated to building a hierarchical progression of knowledge, based on reproducible observation and carefully crafted, proven, cause-and-effect explanation.

Science is a consistent method of study and description. Science is based on the assumption that the universe is founded on a physics that is real and reliable, not necessarily fixed, but predictable. The ultimate cornerstone of science is the creation of theories (explanations) that are subject to test and verification. Claimed explanations that are not amenable to validation are unacceptable, so that all hypotheses must be converted to a testable form to be of any utility. A strong corollary is that results of experiments must be reproducible. A study developed by one person or group that cannot be repeated by others fails to achieve legitimate status. Finally, the means of addressing voids in our knowledge is critical. Hypotheses (unproved conjectures) are perfectly acceptable, if labeled as such, and in fact, novel hypotheses that are testable have become revered as the fuel of progress. Suppositions that are subject to investigation are the driving force of continuing study and the cross-fertilization of ideas.

Most look back on the world view of the aboriginal mind, with its overwhelming mystical content, as being detached from what we see today as reality. But we should not be so smug. Modern humans are not coupled so tightly to reality either. We are literally immersed in science and exploit its fruits every minute of every day. But, unrealistically, our world view is still predominantly religious. This does not mean that we are factional in demeanor, although some people are. Rather, Western humanity typically exhibits a world view featuring some sense of the soul, a personal relation to a human-like god, a god that is both benevolent and omnipotent, and other features that we shall show are inconsistent with knowledge or reason. Our ingrained minds have not caught up with our way of life or the state of our knowledge.

What Is Religion?

Religion represents the relation of humans to that which is regarded as holy. In general, modern religions, especially those of a Western bent, are focused on a deity, but also entail much more. Basic characteristics of most religions include the activity of worship, promulgation of standards or codes of moral conduct, unquestioning adherence and allegiance to a central system of belief, behavior that is controlled and/or ritualistic, celebration of certain ancestors, leaders, organizations, places and/or things, and adherence to various social constraints, activities and practices. Such elements are carried out by many believers and worshipers and are usually founded on alleged truths from the past, dictated by religious authorities and scriptures.

Although the exact content varies considerably between major organizations, the majority of the above components are sacred to most religions.

It is obvious to virtually anyone that an objective look across the broad array of religions reveals extreme diversity of detail. At the highest level, of course, often profound differences can be seen between major contemporary religions, such as Catholicism, Protestantism, Judaism, Islam and Hinduism. But the differences go much deeper. Even within a given religion, major differences proliferate at the levels of primary divisions, progressively subordinate levels of authority, and even within individual groups or denominations. The total spectrum of religious entities having identifiably distinct systems and views is enormous. As the criteria for religious distinctions are liberalized, thereby basing distinction on smaller and smaller differences, the number of religious units, on an order-of-magnitude basis, explodes. Today, liberal accountings of distinct religious entities might reveal counts that approach or exceed the 5,000 or so spoken languages of the earth.

Religious thought has been found within groups characterized by the mythical mind that lived as long as 50,000 to 100,000 years ago (see Chapter 6). Primordial religious activities appear to have been intertwined with myth and ritual. In seeking explanations for observed phenomena, elements of nature supposedly came to be revered as representing and revealing to human groups various dimensions of reality. Also, evidence associated with early and mid-term mythical groups implicating Deification, or a personification of hidden forces, has been widespread. It would appear that the oldest deities in most cultures were sky gods, but animal gods and prominent landscape features (mountains, rivers, bodies of water, etc.) also exhibited early popularity. Later, upon the invention of agriculture, the anthropological record indicates the advent of new structures of the sacred. Initial reverence of plants seems to have led later to the honoring of fertility in plants, certain domesticated animals and humans. And eventually, based on some interpretations of the known record, the life, death and rebirth of plants may have set the stage for broader concepts of death and resurrection, including that of humans.

Religions have, in the course of history, generally been repeatedly forced to reinterpret past dogma in the light of new knowledge or unforeseen problems. Many of the most contentious and bitter religious controversies have been waged between strict conservatives who adhered to traditional prescriptions versus revisionists who sought to adjust moral and/or ceremonial elements in step with ever mounting established fact. Over time, substantial adaptation has transpired, stretching the credibility of many commandments, beliefs, rituals and stipulated behavior patterns. But across all religions and in spite of their associated internal struggles, the maintenance of moral consciousness has remained a primary driving force in the relationship of humans to what is regarded as holy.

Contrasting Science and Religion

Since we became human, our lineage has marveled at the beauty, grandeur and apparently cunning brilliance of the physical universe. Only with the coming of true science in the last four hundred years though, has any highly organized activity been established to study the nature of human existence and its role in the universe at large.

The success of science to date in amassing a breathtaking panorama of nature's detail and ingenuity often masks another startling result — science is not just an arbitrary collection of independent successes, it really works! As more and more knowledge comes to light, it is found that what appeared to be and was often treated as distinct fields in the past come to be viewed as merely two perspectives on one underlying and highly integrated system of truths. People of science tend to take the discipline for granted, because application of the scientific method becomes literally a way of life. On the other hand, the average person has a poor understanding of science, regards many products or assertions of science with some suspicion, and appears unaware that science has largely undermined the religious world view.

Science began to conflict with religion four hundred years ago when the true science of today began to take hold. A clear illustration is the imprisonment and persecution of Galileo by catholic authority in the sixteenth century for his support of the Copernican theory that the planets are sun-centric. The problem was that science began to discredit or dismember certain cherished religious beliefs. For one, the world was revealed to behave in accordance with regular physical laws, removing the need to invoke divine intervention as an explanation. In addition, the earth was shown not to be the center of the solar system, but merely one of several planets that all orbited the sun in a regular fashion. Humanity was also removed from the center stage of the universe, becoming inconsequential passengers in a huge universal machine. In response, the average person saw the upstart science as a substantial threat, a view perpetuated to this day by recalcitrant theologians, religious conservatives, educational system indifference, and poor dissemination by scientists of knowledge to the populace.

Some insight can perhaps be gained by viewing both religion and science relative to two contrasting dimensions: the scholastic and the social. Socially, both religion and science display shortcomings. Science has brought considerable good through the creation of knowledge, evolution of technology, and improvement of general health. In turn, science has also produced weapons and killing systems far beyond earlier comprehension, and has led to modern societies that are stressful and unsettling to many individuals. But religions have inflicted even worse nightmares on humanity. While many religious activities are truly laudable, religious authority has often come to be associated more with power and politics than with good and evil. It is a supreme tragedy that the great religions in recent times are more oriented toward hatred and smoldering if not blatant hostility toward other groups than toward curing mankind's ills and suffering. Glaring examples are current or recent conflicts in Ireland, Bosnia, the Middle East, and Kashmir, all of which have fundamental religious undercurrents. The world certainly needs a universal moral code. But religions impose much other heavy and apparently pointless baggage, and seem incapable of maturing to the point of being appropriate social vehicles for worldwide moral stability.

Turning to the scholastic dimension, throughout history, religion was the seat of doctrine regarding existence. However, as the renaissance in knowledge advanced, science intruded more and more on deeply entrenched religious convictions, such as the dogma of earth's creation in seven days, and the earth as the center of the universe. The not unlikely result has been the appearance and cultivation of the notion that religion and science are irreconcilable and antagonistic. On the one hand, early religious attempts to squelch scientific endeavor have created strong suspicion in the scientific community. In turn, science has undermined much sacred religious teachings and is chastised by many of the faithful.

Thus, religions place extreme reliance on history and tradition, often to the point of obsession. In fact the usual retort to a challenge of any dogma is that such doctrine is revealed truth from the past and cannot be challenged. But, paradoxically, as we have seen, the great religions do in fact change with time, often substantially — they must, to survive. The dilemma is that the central most elements of a given religion typically cannot be changed, because alteration of such key cornerstones might mark the end of the road. So modern religions are largely trapped by indefensible core dogma, and basically strive to control people rather than save them. The deterioration is not caused by the faithful masses that seek and practice religion. Many worshipers and religious practitioners are exemplary in mind and behavior and true to the cause. But the religious institutions and leadership appear to be causing more problems than they are solving, and the wounds are self-inflicted.

Science is not perfect either. Many problems exist in science, including excessive pressure for scientists to produce. The old adage of 'publish or perish' continues rising to new and frightening heights as funding pressures mount in education and government. Also, a small minority of supposed scientists do not always properly practice the art, creating or distorting data for personal advantage. But science has one superlative attribute. Religion looks backward to ancient dogma and revealed fact, and professes to represent immutable albeit unverifiable truth. In stark contrast, science is pointed ever forward to the systematized revelation of new, proven knowledge. Science is the only system of thought that glorifies verified advancement. The built-in facility for science to accommodate change as new discoveries come to light generates, in my mind, profound power, vitality and endurance. Science is open-ended and pregnant with tremendous possibilities for the future, in a fashion quite analogous to self-organizing nature itself.

There has been a strong tendency for people to portray the struggle between science and religion in terms of 'right' and 'wrong.' It is true that most scientists do not accept religious dogma, although people of science also do not perceive religion as a threat in the way that scientists are perceived as menacing by the religious. But a right-versus-wrong mentality obscures other possibilities. A few scientists are agnostic, and so have no problem whatsoever reconciling religion and science. Many other scientists are religious in the traditional sense, but have learned to keep religion and science in separate realms or have developed liberalized religious beliefs to allow harmony with science. Finally, there are many scientists that are not religious in the conventional way, but nevertheless subscribe to a deep inner sense that nature is not only incredibly inspiring but also purposeful. Some of the latter group feel further that the universe is not an accident and that humans somehow have a role to play in the grandeur of the world. After much research, I must confess allegiance to the latter circle.

Is God Necessary?

Without any intent of disrespect, another approach to gain insight about the question of existence is to inquire about whether god is really necessary. In other words, given our newfound (albeit still incomplete) understanding of the universe, grounded in natural law at every level and at every moment, is there a need for god? Of course the faithful perceive miracles all around and point to such wonders as signs of ongoing divine intervention. But all such happenings are heavily draped in emotional overtones and a fierce desire on the part of the relevant observers for the miracles to be true. And, to date, no alleged miracle has ever been verified scientifically.

There are numerous books in the popular science literature that describe in intimate detail the immense interrelated complexity of the universe and how natural law defines actions of every sort. Relevant examples are presented under 'Suggested Readings' at the end of the book. The known laws of nature unfold in a dazzling and seemingly brilliant fashion, so beautiful in symmetry and, once understood, simplicity that intelligent design seems intrinsic and obvious to most. The present discussion is certainly indebted to the many splendid insightful descriptions of the physical world which have recently appeared. Importantly, the popular science literature has shown tremendous growth in the last decade. This trend is very encouraging and also essential. For people to have an honest world view of their own choosing, it is imperative that all of the facts be laid out in full view, including religious, scientific and philosophical.

So the universe appears to have been designed. But does that automatically call into play a personified designer? Most religious teachings to date depict god as omnipotent, implying free reign to create anything at all from a large if not infinite spectrum of options. But the latter must be qualified by requiring that the resulting rules of interaction (laws of nature) be logically consistent, since that is what we observe. So the choice of universes is not so free after all, but actually quite constrained. Also, the incessant advance of science is providing a mounting sense of a possible grand convergence, as described in Chapter One, toward one unifying Theory Of Everything. It may turn out that multiple alternatives to structuring the universe just don't exist. Rather, there may be one unique exalted truth, one supreme logical principle, from which all else follows. Given the revelations of modern science that: a) the world we know requires an incredibly delicate balance between diverse quantitative relationships (constants of nature; see Chapter 10): and b) that nature appears mischievous but brilliant and extremely rigorous, I would personally be surprised if in fact there is not but one choice.

So where would such a world leave god? It is interesting that virtually every religion teaches that god is a mind. In any case, we have developed elsewhere the concept that god does not appear to intercede in the moment-by-moment unfolding of nature. Furthermore, the universe does not seem to have an exact blueprint that is being followed. Rather, the world appears to be rich with potentialities, and evolution seems to spontaneously proceed, constrained only by internally consistent natural laws. Finally, as developed immediately above, there may have been no freedom of choice in the design of the original universe, the existent natural laws and perhaps the initial conditions being dictated by logical necessity.

But even such a scenario does not in the slightest degree deny god, if by the concept of god we mean that which is the supreme controlling influence of the universe. In this book, as you have probably noticed, that is exactly what god is taken to mean. So the present approach suggests that we at least consider an alternative to the traditional vision of god, from that of the ultimate master administrator who creates universes, controls events and breaks physical laws at will, to a universal mind incorporated into nature in a way that nature and god are really different aspects of the same system.

The result would be a natural god, not a supernatural god. Would that be so bad? Quite the contrary, it seems to me far more elegant and personally engaging to contemplate the possibility of my consciousness being an actual part of both a universal mind and an internally consistent universal megasystem. For contrast, the most distinctive alternative would be to view myself as an independent being vying for the attention of a master controller within a universe that is a part of neither entity.

Importantly, it appears that we inhabit a physical universe where every bit of today's tremendous diversity was inherent in a system astonishingly simple at its origin. At the earliest times during the big bang, a few types of primordial particles (in staggering quantities) and a large amount of incredibly intense radiation represented all that there was. Since then, every last one of the countless, spectacular components of the present universe apparently evolved and unfolded automatically. The design of such a colossal, self-evolving system with inherently immense yet undefined diversity and potential would, to me, represent a stupendous intellectual and practical accomplishment. Personally, I find a self-unfolding system to be far more impressive than the layout of a contrived universe, where physical laws are suspended at the will of a supernatural controller to permit the selective manipulation or override of any existing evolution.

Of course, everyone must make up his or her own mind. But both our very existence and our personal relationship with god are issues far too important to be founded on limited perspective. We should not accept either past dogma or currently accepted fact on blind faith without critical personal evaluation.

How Long will the Universe Last?

The idea of a natural god raises the issues of when the universe began and when it might end. The reason is that a mind, even a universal one, requires organization. And yet, from Chapter 3, the Second Law of Thermodynamics (the Second Law) states that all useful organization incessantly declines with time to a point eventually where no useful action is possible.

In other words, the Second Law says that all capabilities to perform useful work (influence) will ultimately vanish. The inevitable 'friction' (inefficiencies) inescapably inherent in every action will ultimately consume all useful energy. The latter process is termed the temperature death (or heat death) of the universe. Temperature differences between systems imply an ability to do useful work, and the ultimate fate of the universe will be the progression of everything to a vanishing low uniform temperature where no useful work is possible. The heat death is not disputed — the Second Law is considered one of the cornerstones of all of science.

Cosmology means the study of the nature and temporal course of the universe. Several major types of cosmology have been thoroughly studied in the twentieth century. But, now, we see almost universal support for one cosmology class, those that feature the big bang.

The purported beginning of the universe, the big bang, has been well documented in the popular science literature, is supported by overwhelming scientific data and consensus, and will be accepted here as a given. As the story goes, the universe is now undergoing a major expansion, still flying apart from the explosion of the big bang. But the expansion rate is slowly declining, so we must consider at least two possibilities relative to the future: a) the expansion may continue forever, to achieve the conditions of a temperature or heat death (as mutual gravitational attraction between all universe constituents slows but does not stop the dispersion of everything); or b) gravity may eventually stop and then reverse the expansion, leading to an ultimate collapse recreating conditions of the big bang (a process termed the big crunch). Actually, a third possibility exists as well. The universe may be expanding at a perfect rate to forever approach the point of stasis, at a slower and slower rate, but to never achieve stasis even over an infinite time. However, in the subject instance, the ultimate result would be the same as that for the first case, a general expansion that continues forever.

Whether a slow temperature death (heat death) or a distant big crunch is the more likely prediction depends on as-yet-unavailable cosmological data that is expected to come to light within the next decade. In addition, the simple model of one universe expanding, or first expanding and then collapsing, are only two of many vying cosmologies. Alternative models include cyclic evolution of the universe through repeated big bang and big crunch episodes, multiple parallel universes, and others. Finally, although rejected by virtually all current cosmologists, a steady-state universe is mentioned here for completeness, a hypothesis outside the class of big bang models and more popular in decades past. Steady-state cosmologies depend on the widespread creation of new matter as the universe expands, resulting in the maintenance of a constant average matter density as the universe grows in size. At our present state of knowledge, it is not possible to completely and logically select between the proposed or perhaps yet-to-be-offered possibilities. But it can be said that only universes of the cyclic or steady-state types would allow a natural god to be eternal.

The Pivotal Role of Mathematics

Lying at the very heart of science is mathematics. The unique language of science is, in fact, mathematics. Our confident certainty of known relationships springs from the ubiquitous symbolic language of mathematics, being at once very broad based but also exquisite in the exclusion of ambiguity and doubt. Mathematics is rigorous in formulation and in expression, and is generally universal across spoken languages. Mathematics is the only language with an intrinsic logic, and that logic has been honed to a superlative degree to avoid misinterpretation and miscommunication.

But let's ask what may seem like a strange question at first — why does mathematics work? What is there about the physical world that lends itself to mathematical description?

Through endless observations and experiments, we have come to find that the world is quite regular in behavior. The systematization of discovered aspects of the world that are predictable is what we call science. Science codifies observation, and the language employed is mathematics.

Mathematics really works. From humble beginnings of counting and accounting in the developing mythic mind of primitive societies, the discipline has grown to cover all of quantitative science. At a more mundane level, mathematics also plays a significant role in the lives of the average citizen. The reason is that the use of mathematics has endowed human discourse with elements essential to even common interaction and understanding. We couldn't live like we do without math.

But, a reason is not necessarily an explanation. Why should the gravitational attraction exerted on objects by the earth, or exerted by an object anywhere on other objects, terrestrial or otherwise, be directly proportionate to precisely certain measured quantities, everywhere and everywhere. Is this coincidence, or does mathematics really represent a deep-seated reality of nature? Put another way, did we humans discover mathematics, that is, was it intrinsically there all along? Or is mathematics a human invention of convenience, but not really representative of the nature of nature.

Mathematics can be viewed pragmatically as a giant analogy, but one that never falters. All of science has not revealed even one physical phenomenon that cannot be described mathematically. So which system is real? Is nature actually the analogy, representing particular material embodiments of an underlying mathematical reality? Or is nature the most real, with mathematics forming an abstract model? In other words, is math the analogy of nature, or is nature the analogy of math? Frankly, at the present time, we don't know!

This astonishing state of affairs is at once both fascinating and embarrassing. In conducting their professional endeavors, scientists work as if it is mathematics that is being discovered. The operative assumption is that mathematical relationships describe inherent pre-existing properties of the universe. Scientists usually don't think much about mathematics itself, but use it as a tool for whatever effort is underway. In addition, some mathematics is invented simply for invention's sake, with no direct purpose in mind. The latter activity continually expands an elaborate body of mathematical thought that extends, we think, beyond the known boundaries of nature. But it is amazing and, actually, spooky that many mathematical formulations that were purely abstract and supposedly detached from reality when developed, have been found later to represent an essential description for some newly described feature of reality. Two classic examples from the nineteenth century are instructive. First, James Maxwell predicted the existence of radio waves mathematically, in the process of deriving the equations to describe the electromagnetic field, decades prior to the discovery of radio waves. Second, early in the twentieth century, Albert

Einstein employed a non-Euclidean geometry as the basis for his theory of general relativity, a space-time description that was invented by Bernhard Reimann long before Einstein was born. But Reimann was purely exploring mathematical abstractions, with no idea whatsoever that his model would lead to the best space-time description to the present day.

There is a Touch of Religion in Science

Religion is rooted in the past and is based on blind-faith, whereas science moves into the future founded on reason and proven fact. However, a problem lurks within science. The entire edifice of science is built on mathematics, and yet we really don't understand math's origin. Is mathematics discovered or invented? We just don't know for sure.

My personal instinct is that mathematics is discovered, not invented. But the extreme view of the discovery school says that reality is mathematics and nothing more, that there really is no substance but just relationships between abstract entities that our minds render as tangible. That is a little strong for me personally. However, my hunch is that mathematics reveals something about the deepest structure of the universe, that the ultimate underpinnings of the world are interrelated in a way that is equivalent or directly analogous to inter-actions that are somehow computational in nature.

I am swayed by several bits of meaningful but circumstantial evidence. First is the tremendous success of mathematics in describing the world at abso-lutely every level. Second, as mentioned, many marvelous constructs devel-oped initially for pure mathematical beauty, symmetry, or other features, but with no purpose or application in mind whatsoever, have been found later to form seemingly the best means to describe startling new physical discoveries. Third, mathematics is only one of several systems of thought (e.g., religious, metaphysical, philosophical, atheistic, cult-based constructs, etc.) used in an attempt to describe the universe, but the rest have fared very poorly while math-ematics has flourished. Finally, once a certain level of theoretical sophistica-tion had been achieved, mathematics has in many decisive instances led the way to new physical discoveries (e.g., quarks, black holes, electromagnetic waves, lasers, transistors) through extrapolation or departure from previous models. But regardless of my personal leanings, the facts to date regarding whether math is discovered or invented are certainly open to interpretation. More data is needed for an accurate differentiation.

So, mathematics works extremely well, but its ultimate foundation is uncer-tain. Since mathematics is the language of science, a modicum of faith is there-fore required to believe in science. In a sense, then, science (mathematics) is to a certain extent a religious-like system of belief. All of our most powerful knowledge about the nature and structure of the universe is ultimately specified mathematically, and yet we don't understand math's origin. The contrast between science and formal religion is that future study may very well define the origin of mathematics, whereas theology is precariously trapped between an ordained immutable past that conflicts more and more with growing established fact.

Despite the lingering requirement for a touch of faith, there are several reasons science commands the high ground, compared to religion, in the search for a realistic world view. Science encourages critical review and analysis of beliefs and honors the advancement of knowledge. In fact, science relentlessly challenges the state-of-the-art in a healthy and constructive fashion to extend and expand our knowledge. Also, science demands independent verification by autonomous observers to avoid errors of information or interpretation. Science seeks not only to describe events or processes but to understand mechanisms of action, to explain the how and why. So the real goal of science is tangible knowledge that we can check, understand, and use, not unverifiable beliefs and intuitions. Finally, religions impose a world view, whereas science naturally develops a world view as the result of global interpretations of countless discovered facts.

So, at least the religions of today offer weak credibility regarding promulgation of their respective world views. Present day religions also do not compare favorably with the potent and rapidly growing prowess of science to advance knowledge and understanding, and the general world view that is coalescing therefrom.

Extraterrestrial Life & the Challenge to Religion

Much of what has been said may be taken by some to mean that science categorically refutes religion. But the purpose here has not been to attack religion. Rather, the goal has been to generically present religion in the context of a broader point of view consistent with the explosion of relevant modern scientific evidence.

To retain credibility, religions must almost certainly change. Religious survival will probably be dependent on reconnecting with the masses and in developing and promulgating a world view that is in step with ever mounting fact. My sense is that, generally, members of Western society currently suffer from a fractured mind-set. We are permeated by ingrained structure of religious origin in our personal world view, but we adopt a pragmatic and sometimes amoral exploitation of science and other people in the conduct of our everyday affairs. In our search for god, we as humanity must reach a world view featuring concurrence and harmony between our deepest beliefs, our behavior, and known fact. I think science rather than religion will lead the way.

As developed in Chapter 4, scientists generally believe that life is yet another natural form of ordinary matter. New evidence has narrowed the time interval near earth's beginning to the point that a geologically short period of perhaps less than 200 million years was available for pre-cellular life to evolve to the cellular level. The existence of evolved life in general, and such a rapid rise from inanimate matter in particular, flames the fire of speculation about other life in the universe.

Current evidence concerning the existence of extraterrestrial life was discussed in Chapter 4. The conclusion was that it would be unlikely for their not to be life elsewhere. If we accept that life did evolve naturally on earth, then to assert that we exist in the only privileged location and time in the entire universe would be a difficult proposition to defend.

Previously, the concept was also developed that intelligent life beyond earth, some far superior and precedent to humans, is very likely. But it is easy for dissenters to dismiss an unproved hypothesis of extraterrestrial life. In contrast, the actual discovery of life external to the earth having intelligence approximating or exceeding the self-conscious state of today's humans would confront religion with a monumental problem. The entire foundation of many religions is built on a unique relationship between god and humans. The latter notion is incompatible with a universe where life is ubiquitous, spontaneously evolving when and where certain required natural conditions are met. Importantly, the idea of widespread life was given a substantial boost by the recent purported discovery of evidence suggesting past microbial life on Mars. NASA's planned return of Martian soil and rock samples to earth early in the next century may contribute further insight.

Finally, research is underway to explore ways that pre-cellular evolution may have occurred. Laboratory proof that life springs from inanimate matter through completely natural processes would represent a profound discovery. Such a finding would provide a provocative clue supporting the evolutionary origin of earth life and of the potential for widespread life evolving elsewhere in the universe. Further, if the purported development on earth of self-organized self-consciousness stands the test of time, the likelihood of widespread intelligence in the universe becomes a distinct possibility. In the spirit of the latter thoughts, then, the next chapter probes deeper into the relation between the mind and the universe.

Chapter 9
The Central Role of Consciousness

Human Importance

At one extreme, we have seen science blamed for relegating humankind to an inconsequential state. Central to the latter position has been the portrayal of science as showing humans to be minuscule and insignificant bystanders in a gigantic, indifferent universal machine.

This book attempts to paint a totally opposite portrait. Chapter after chapter has been devoted to building a foundation for human importance. Daunting evidence has been reviewed that shows how matter reacts in very controlled ways according to perpetual natural laws. And built into the controlling physics is incredible potential for emerging properties and for self-organization of matter, both non-living and alive, that can produce awesome complexity. On earth, in occurrences numbering far beyond comprehension, small, select, individual self-organizing events have been captured in enduring form, and have combined and compounded to realize life and to evolve higher life forms. And it would appear that all of this happened automatically, through spontaneous interplay of properties of matter, physical laws and chance happenstance, without dependence on a preordained blueprint.

But by far the most spectacular result of the earthly drama of naturally unfolding nature is the appearance of humans. The dazzling theatrics of the universe at large is a fabulous show that is absolutely wasted on pre-human life. At least this appears true from the earthly vantage point. On first order, there doesn't seem to be much point to the universe, unless some intelligence arises to at least observe and appreciate the sensational display.

Of course, the cosmic show is not easy to see from our seats in the audience, at least unaided. Many feel deep awe and perhaps an emotional twinge when we look at the star-studded sky on a clear night. Certainly the experience is even more impressive away from the major cities and other havens of air pollution and interfering lights. But a quite misleading feature is that the scene appears basically static (ignoring daily and annual rhythms). The stars appear set in a fixed pattern relative to one another, and the only dynamics are the slow (measured in days, months and years) movement of the sun, moon and planets and the darting paths of occasional meteors and shooting stars.

The real cosmic show can only be appreciated by the use of telescopes. Suddenly, the cosmos is revealed as an incredibly dynamic landscape, with evidence of momentous forces and processes at work virtually everywhere we care to look. The tapestry of the universe is ever changing, and only looks static to the unaided eye due to the incredible distances involved.

Actually, even with the most powerful telescopes, the expanses of space are so enormous that we rarely perceive movement even then. The only exception is for certain nearby objects in the solar system or its near neighborhood that are therefore incredibly close to the earth. In general, our evidence of cosmic dynamics comes from the way objects look as if caught at some point in ongoing activities, and from observing countless different systems that collectively reveal various stages of particular processes. Such data can basically be creatively arranged into what we suspect are frame-by-frame series, allowing us to piece together theories of cosmic action that prove to be unbelievably diverse. And yet, in spite of massive differentiation, the mounting evidence reveals deep interconnections and simplicities and also spectacular underlying order.

It should be safe to say that we consider our human condition to represent substantial intelligence. And as reviewed previously, especially in Chapter 4, a strong argument can be built in support of the likely existence of intelligent life elsewhere. Additionally, some such life is almost certainly far advanced in intelligence compared to humans. Most people who study the universe come away with a feeling that the magnificence of cosmic organization must have profound meaning. The rest of the present book is directed to probing that tantalizing issue.

Implications of the Anthropic Principle

But why are we here? We marvel at the beautiful fabric of the universe. However, celestial magnificence does little to explain human existence. In fact, there is absolutely no known data that compels the existence of any form of life anywhere.

Chapter 8 included a discussion of one extreme cosmology that depicted humans as incidental accidents of an omnipresent universal physical machine indifferent to life. One opposing cosmological limit is some form of human-centered system tailor-made by god for us. The latter idea has formed a cornerstone for many societies, peaking amidst English scientists in the eighteenth century. The persuasion was seen to retain prominence until Charles Darwin and Alfred Russel Wallace developed the theory of natural selection in the mid-nineteenth century. The theory of natural selection precipitated among scientists a permanent rejection of the thought that evolution is goal-directed.

It is a clear fact that we can only observe a universe that is consistent with human existence. There is only one universe that we can see, and that's where we live. If the universe were incompatible with humans or to earth-like organic life in general, then we would not be here to observe the resultant world. The link between the occurrence of human observers and the requisite limits on permissible laws and conditions of the universe (cosmologies) that allow suitable conditions for observers to exist has come to be dubbed the Anthropic Principle.

In the simple form outlined above, the Anthropic Principle does not claim that human existence uniquely compels the observed physical laws nor a world deliberately designed to evolve humans. However, it has been established beyond any reasonable doubt that even minute changes to key laws of nature would render the universe devoid of organic observers, through all of space and time. This startling fact, which almost certainly has profound meaning, is discussed in more detail below.

The Weak Anthropic Principle. Modern science has revealed a mysterious truth about the universe. In the mathematical language of science, the current description of the universe involves a large number of parameters (specific physical variables, such as subatomic particle masses, atomic dimensions, etc.), structural relationships (the ratios of atomic element occurrences in nature; the ratio of the electric charge of an electron to its mass; and so forth), and constants (e.g., the Newtonian gravitational constant, the speed of light; etc.). It has been known for some time that particular attributes of nature are extremely critical. For if certain properties had deviated in some cases by even vanishingly small amounts, the universe as we know it could not have existed at all. In turn, if the universe differed much from the one we inhabit, as mentioned above, we would not be here to bask in its splendor. The true meaning of this humbling finding is not as yet known.

The above concept, that there are universe designs in which we would not expect to be present to observe, is termed the Weak Anthropic Principle. The principle applies not only to earth bound life, but to life as we know it anywhere in the universe. In fact, without some extremely special circumstances, a universe capable of supporting organized organic systems could not exist.

Another viewpoint is instructive. Picture an ensemble made up of an infinite number of alternative universes. Consider that all possibilities are represented, that is, every combination of age, size, temperature, shape, content, ratios of forces, constants of nature, initial conditions, and so forth. Then, what percentage of said universes would be capable of supporting organic observers like us? It turns out that the percentage appears to be very small indeed, far, far below one percent. As only one of innumerable possible examples, if the strengths of the four forces of nature were changed only slightly, chemistry as we know it becomes impossible. With no chemistry, stars cannot form, which means that carbon and other key molecules of life are not even created, and therefore observers do not evolve. And there are a host of other physical parameters of nature that, just like the strengths of the four forces, must be nearly as we find them in our present universe, often to exquisite precision (see Chapter 10 for another detailed illustration), or organic life could not exist. Thus, except in extraordinary circumstances, each universe in our hypothetical array would be sterile.

The Weak Anthropic Principle certainly represents a major truth. Just how restrictive are the limits on viable worlds is an open question. Recall that the discussion of Chapter 8 mentioned the intriguing possibility that there might be only one possible universe, dictated by a single self-consistent logical principle.

In any case, consider for the moment that the universe is infinitely large, a notion favored by current data and consensus, and that the initial conditions (the nature, state, position and motion of all primordial constituents) of the universe were random. Realize also that, in such a system, sporadically created pockets of relatively concentrated material would occasionally grow large enough to begin attracting more and more material in, eventually, a runaway local positive feedback fashion. In some cases, such entities could grow to become island universes, and each island world would likely contain some relatively unique conditions. Conceptually, there are even ways envisioned that the physics might be different in distinct island universes. Either way, the observable universe that we see from earth may merely be a portion of one tiny island world in a much larger or infinite universe. We would be the lucky beneficiaries of precise conditions for the unlikely recipe necessary for our existence.

The Strong Anthropic Principle. So, the reality is that a long list of exquisitely tuned properties and relationships must hold for the universe to be able to contain organic observers. The specific parameter values required seem coincidental to us now, because we have not as yet gained the necessary knowledge to derive every relationship from first principles. But the advance of science is chipping away at the remaining 'arbitrary' factors, and new theories now under intense study portend the possibility for major advances.

The amazing restrictions placed on alternative world structures led astrophysicist Brandon Carter to propose a more metaphysical posture to the universe that he labeled the Strong Anthropic Principle. The Strong Anthropic Principle states that, due to the large and seemingly disparate coincidences in the makeup of the universe which are prerequisite to organic living beings, eventual intelligent life in the universe is postulated to be an absolute necessity. In other words, nature organizes itself in a fashion to guarantee the universe becomes self-aware. Thus, whereas the Weak Anthropic Principle places boundary conditions on possible systems otherwise free to self-organize, the Strong Anthropic Principle imposes an added organizing stipulation that preordains intelligent life.

The main tenets of the Weak Anthropic Principle are certainly true. Our human existence places constraints on the types of permissible universes, because the universe we populate obviously produced humans. On the other hand, the Strong Anthropic Principle is far less secure. The consensus of modern scientists rejects the position that the evolution of life on earth, and by extension, in the universe, is predetermined. Such a teleological idea, that there is some specific goal toward which nature is inexorably advancing, following a preordained blueprint, whether related to living or non-living material, is not supported by known fact. The consensus view is that the Anthropic Principle merely identifies coincidences in physical law necessary for life to have evolved, but steps beyond the bounds of present understanding if extended to say that the genesis of conscious observers is an absolute requirement.

Level Upon Level of Appended Organization

Chapters 2 and 3 were devoted to the concepts of emerging properties and self-organizing systems. Considerable attention was paid to the two subjects, because both concepts bring to light critical understanding for the present and the next (final) chapter.

Chapters 2 and 3 showed that the two processes, emerging properties and self-organization, are certainly similar on the surface. But emerging properties were defined as a broad generic umbrella for any emerging attribute. Examples include the phenomena of pressure, temperature and sound that emerge from huge numbers of rapidly moving, randomly interacting atoms or molecules in a gas, and also the phenomenon of color which is merely a differential analysis of different frequencies in a light wave that is otherwise homogeneous. In contrast, self-organization was depicted as an elite subset of emerging properties where demanding conditions are often required for initial formation and ongoing energy is required to sustain the new special organization. Life, a pot of simmering soup, and the collective behavior of an ant colony or bee hive are self-organizing systems.

One of the themes of this book is that nature is characterized by layer upon layer of appended complexity. This hierarchy of complexity has only recently come to be appreciated as a general rule of nature. It's not that layers of adaptation on top of adaptation had not been recognized earlier, say, in the comparative anatomy between existing and/or extinct species, for example. It was well known that evolution built on what existed before, rather than starting anew, when novel features were derived. But a broader perspective picturing the world as the grand adapter, with the progressive grafting of fresh complexity onto lower-level systems pervading all of nature, is only now coming to be recognized. And as will be reviewed in the next section, new findings and interpretations suggest that nature may be even more tightly integrated than the generally accepted view of modern physics.

As one ascends the layers of complexities in some systems, an intriguing thing happens. Often, a knowledge of the rules of behavior at lower levels provides little help in deciphering actions and interrelationships at higher tiers. As an illustration from the subject matter of Chapter 2, an entity such as a hydrogen molecule, when studied in collections of larger and larger groups of such atoms, reveals the gradual emergence of the phenomenon of sound waves. Characterization of the emergent phenomena of sound requires different modes of description than that used to study individual molecules. Molecules are characterized by such parameters as molecular weight, electron orbitals, quantum energy levels, and so forth. Sound waves, on the other hand, are classified according to parameters like intensity, waveform, wavelength, and velocity, and the properties of individual molecules in the system are typically irrelevant.

An important lesson here is that the best understanding of system behavior in any given situation can be quite dependent upon the hierarchical tier examined, that is on the level of descriptive abstraction employed. In many cases, and especially for the interesting situations relative to self-organization, life, and consciousness, different laws come into play as new phenomena emerge. For instance, the gas law describing the interplay of pressure, temperature and volume in a closed system,

$$PV = nRT,$$

where   P = Pressure;
        V = Volume;
        n = a proportionality constant;
        R = the Gas Constant; and
        T = Temperature;

which is the ultimate defining relationship at the level of the bulk gas, has no meaning at the single molecule tier of description.

Thus, as we climb to higher and higher levels of abstraction, we can likely expect the need to discover new laws of nature. From time to time, the new laws will show little if any resemblance to the lower level laws that we hold dear. For many instances in the past, leaps of genius were sometimes required to bring the next higher level of abstraction into the realm of understanding. The discoveries of Quantum Theory and Relativity Theory early in the twentieth century are clear examples. In a like manner, in the future pursuit of even higher levels of abstraction and understanding, incredible innovation may be needed to even conceive a reasonable framework for the heralded problems facing science today (e.g., pursuit of the Theory of Everything; characterizing the origin of life on earth; finding evidence of extraterrestrial life; coming to understand god from a factual basis, defining the mechanisms of consciousness and self-consciousness, etc.).

Beyond Individual Consciousness

One example of an emerging property of the mind is human behavior. Here we can show a vivid illustration near the pinnacle of earth bound layered complexity, having different laws applicable at virtually every rung of the hierarchical ladder of abstraction. Just the mention of a few tiers embellished with an illustrative scientific discipline of relevance will convey the point: atoms (quantum mechanics); molecules (molecular biology); molecular interactions (biochemistry); cells (cell biology); tissues (the science of tissue culture); organs and organ systems (anatomy, biochemistry and physiology of the brain and nervous system); and the conscious human organism (cognitive science; psychology). The latter list is quite cursory and also arbitrary. Exhaustive scrutiny could produce an immense roster of tiers from which to draw.

The top of our illustrative arbitrary hierarchy was defined as, in part, human psychology. We would expect and certainly do find the need for unique laws to properly characterize psychology in all of its many dimensions. Full knowledge (which is not available yet) of brain physiology would not be sufficient, the science of individual organs or their component tissues even less useful, and so forth. Accurate analysis of the high level functional abstraction that we label as psychology requires description by unique laws. Does this mean, then, that psychology rejects the laws of the underlying tiers? Certainly not! The point is that additive elements, making up new types of processes, laws and principles that augment regularities applicable at lower planes, come into play at successively higher levels of organization.

Almost certainly, human self-consciousness is not the supreme level of self-organization possible in the universe. In fact, even right here on earth, a number of obvious examples of higher complexity tiers can be cited, including human behavior in groups (the subject of sociology), language, and literature. Such systems surpass the behavior of individual humans, creating again the need for yet higher laws of description.

But the latter examples are still part of direct human experience. The really exciting, and for some perhaps disquieting, possibilities exist beyond that which we currently know. It is unlikely that we could even render reasonable guesses regarding what might be in store for the earth and its inhabitants. But what is likely is that innumerable, probably countless oases of self-organized intelligence have occurred or now exist elsewhere in the universe. And some fraction of extraterrestrial civilizations have probably ascended to lofty rungs on the ladder of intelligence complexity far beyond that which we have experienced or dreamed.

Mysterious Glimpses of a New Holism

Holism represents the concept that the universe and/or subsystems thereof, and especially systems of high complexity such as living material, can only be properly characterized functionally based on global behavior of the whole entity. The reason is that the highest level system of consideration, the whole, is viewed as being much more than the sum of its parts. Thus, properties or reactions of the whole cannot be derived solely from summation of the properties of its parts. Familiar examples of holism include the behavior of an ant colony compared to the actions of individual ants, bodily versus cell function, medicine treating both the mind and the body, and ecology representing the idea of man and the environment as forming one system.

Based on data and ideas presented earlier, most would agree that concepts like life, cells, mind, and consciousness fit the holistic mold. The latter phenomena cannot be accurately and completely depicted in terms of lower-level description. While the lower-level characterizations are necessary for full perspective, complete understanding must additionally take into account and explain the added spectrum of emerging properties arising at the global level of the entire entity.

We have been talking about systems that show the above form of holism, tied closely to the concepts of emerging properties and self-organization, throughout much of the present book. In stark contrast, a glimpse of some further, totally distinct, previously unsuspected complexity in nature of a seemingly omnipresent holistic stature has surprisingly arisen in recent theory and experiment. The present subsection is intended to provide added background and insight, yet may be found somewhat weighty for the uninitiated reader. In fact, this subsection can be skimmed or omitted without undue effect on the thrust of the book, but provides an insightful and eerie peek at the strangeness of true reality.

For perspective, Einstein's special theory of relativity established the speed of light as a limit on the velocity that information and also cause-and-effect influences can be transmitted through the universe. Extrapolating the latter result, most scientists had historically assumed that the speed of light set a limit on all forms of influence, whether electromagnetic (e.g., light), material, or any other. That tidy thought has recently been shattered, as we shall see.

Albert Einstein, Nathan Rosen and Boris Podolsky proposed a famous thought experiment in 1935 (termed the EPR Paradox, after the author's initials and the dilemma unveiled), intended to undermine the prevailing interpretation of Quantum Theory at the time. A detailed recount is not important here, and will be deferred to the many excellent descriptions found among the Suggested Readings at the end of the book. Importantly, it was necessary for the EPR exercise to be a thought experiment, rather than a real laboratory rendition, because the required test conditions could not be accomplished in 1935.

Recall that Quantum Theory is most powerful in the deep sub-microscopic domain of atoms and subatomic entities. The traditional view of Quantum Theory (originated and championed by Neils Bohr, and called the Copenhagen interpretation for its prime place of development) was that quantum processes (e.g., subatomic particle collisions; particle absorption or emission of electromagnetic radiation; etc.) had to be actually observed before real quantities could be assigned to the targeted properties. In other words, as an illustration, a particle was considered to only have properties such as size (extent), location, or spin if an actual measurement, specifically designed to record the desired property of interest, was carried out. Note that a measurement of location will not provide any information about spin; the observation must be set up to measure spin before any data about spin will appear.

It is critical that we follow these perhaps confusing thoughts further. What the above description really means is that, before a measurement, a given quantum entity is said to exist in an undefined state where all of its measurable attributes exist only as ghostly intangible probabilities, and where there are absolutely no attributes that tangibly exist — in other words, all attributes are ghostly possibilities and nothing is real. However, upon the occurrence of a measurement designed to characterize a specific pre-selected attribute, suddenly, exactly one of the possible values of the pre-selected attribute randomly materializes, and is recorded by the observation. So it appears to the observer that the measured quantity was actually there all the time, but Quantum Theory says that is really not the case. The tangible measured property of, in our example, a pre-selected attribute of the quantum entity, is said to have suddenly appeared from a sea of intangible, unreal potentialities present before the measurement.

Of course, such notions are totally contrary to common sense, but are nevertheless clearly predicted by Quantum Theory. And Quantum Theory is otherwise extremely successful. Along this line of thought, for instance, a quantity called spin is one of several measurable properties of certain subatomic entities (here we use spin for simplification, since that has been the choice for almost all popular accounts, but EPR originally employed an argument based on another attribute). Any such entity certainly has a spin when in fact spin is being measured, but the Copenhagen interpretation of Quantum Theory asserts that the spin is not only unknown but does not even exist unless one actually measures the spin. Put another way, the act of spin measurement creates the tangible manifestation of spin, but it is meaningless to speak about unmeasured spin.

But all of this talk has been about subatomic entities: what does that have to do with ordinary reality? In fact, everything in the universe is made up of quantum entities, either subatomic particles or force quanta (quantum entities that mediate forces between subatomic particles). So Quantum Theory's strange predictions have truly monumental universal implications indeed!

To reiterate, Bohr's view of quantum reality was that no phenomenon could be said to exist until it was observed. In contrast, Einstein had for years been an adamant, outspoken critic of the Copenhagen interpretation. To Einstein, there was a true, tangible reality present whether any observation occurred or not (a view in line with our normal common sense). So, as mentioned, the Einstein-Podolski-Rosen (EPR) thought experiment was a 1935 frontal attack on the Copenhagen interpretation of Quantum Theory. The rationale of the EPR experiment was to analyze the decay of an unstable elementary particle into two photons (photons are the force quanta of the electromagnetic force), a common reaction in subatomic physics termed particle annihilation. At the instant of the decay, all of the energy of the prior particle becomes embodied in two photons that fly apart from the locus of decay at the speed of light in exactly opposite directions. Both photons (as do all photons) possess an intrinsic spin.

Further, due to conservation laws of quantum physics, only two spins are possible, and the spin of one photon must be exactly opposite the other to conserve spin in the decay process, the opposite spins serving to exactly offset one another. But the spin of neither photon is determined (or, according to the Copenhagen interpretation, even exists) until a measurement is made; beforehand, the spins are said to be in an undefined state where all that can be discussed is the probabilities of various spins that could be expected to appear if, and only if, a measurement were to be made. EPR exploited the above facts to demonstrate what they felt was a discrepancy of logic that revealed Quantum Theory to be incomplete, and therefore not a total description of the relevant events (not a total theory).

The EPR experiment pictured the decay of a particle into two photons, and then allowed the resultant photons to fly far apart in opposite directions for, say, one year (so that the photons would be two light years apart, since they would be traveling in opposite directions at the speed of light). In the defined state of separation, the theory of special relativity says that no information can pass between the photons in less than two years (otherwise, travel faster than the speed of light would be required). So far, since neither photon has been subjected to a measurement of spin, the spins of both photons are still undefined. The EPR experiment then imposes a measurement to define the actual spin of just one of the photons. Once the measurement has been completed, of course, the spin of the measured photon is no longer undefined, since the spin is actually known. But the quantum laws dictating the preservation of the total spin of the system now demand that the second photon, the one not subjected to measurement at all and now residing two-light years away, must suddenly undergo a transition to a state with spin exactly opposite to the spin of the measured photon. Otherwise, the conservation of spin of the original decay would be violated.

This astounding conclusion of the EPR thought experiment is certainly contrary to common sense; somehow the unmeasured photon two light years away instantaneously 'knows' that the spin of the partner photon suddenly became defined, and the unmeasured photon then acts accordingly to instantly assume a spin opposite to that of the measured photon. Obviously, the behavior of the unmeasured photon violates all common sense, and seemingly, physics (Quantum Theory) as well. It cannot be overemphasized how sacred conservation laws are in physics and how deeply such laws have been verified. The EPR proposition certainly created a glaring contradiction (the EPR Paradox).

The EPR thought experiment was designed to show that Quantum Theory was incomplete, being unable to properly explain the seeming paradox (the fact that the spin of the unmeasured photon also materialized). The EPR proposal stimulated a tremendous amount of research and was an extremely valuable contribution to science. But, incredibly, the ultimate effect was the opposite of that intended by the EPR authors, as shown below.

Primarily in the 1980s and the 1990s, experiments capturing the essence of the EPR protocol have proven that the proposed EPR outcome, which Einstein and colleagues thought was impossible and therefore would discredit the Copenhagen interpretation, has been repeatedly shown to actually occur! The details are beyond the present discussion (for further information, consult selected works in the 'Suggested Readings'). However, the result has been an incredible demonstration of what is termed a non-local effect. In the EPR-like experiments, what is being observed is an instantaneous influence across space and time that shows particles such as the two photons of EPR to be still physically coupled long after apparently becoming permanently separated.

The full implications of non-locality are not only unknown, but are really only in an early stage of investigation. However, the eventual consequences relative to our understanding of reality are likely to be monumental. As mentioned earlier, the whole universe is ultimately composed of subatomic elements. During early stages of the big bang, ordinary matter did not exist at all, since absolutely everything was in the form of simple subatomic entities, interacting in a stupendous frenzy. A sizable portion of such interactions would have involved non-local effects. The point is that the interconnectedness imposed by non-local reactions during and since the big bang is far beyond the imagination, and points to a major holistic underpinning of the universe unsuspected until quite recently.

Interestingly, in the late 1960s, John Bell derived a mathematical theory predicting that the reality behind experiments like that of EPR must possess non-local features if certain specified conditions were met. It turns out that Quantum Theory meets the conditions required by Bell's model. Furthermore, experiments first completed by Alain Aspect in 1982 and since verified independently prove the validity of Bell's Theorem. Remarkably, Bell's Theorem is so general that it is unconstrained, so that any future, more comprehensive theory of reality, beyond Quantum Theory, will have to comply as well. In general, within the subatomic realm where Quantum Theory reigns, a group of particles must be treated holistically. Therefore, the new holism, in at least the one prominent form represented by non-local interactions of the EPR type, is certainly an essential attribute that any present or future theory of reality must incorporate.

A pivotal question is whether holistic phenomena obey some type of holistic laws distinct from natural law as now known. Many emerging properties can be explained by straightforward mathematical models. As an illustration, the law interrelating pressure, temperature and volume in gases (the gas law; a higher level of abstraction reviewed earlier in the present chapter) can be derived by applying statistical principles to large numbers of linearly moving molecules. But holistic laws might take a different form, based on new organizing drives or forces appearing at higher levels of abstraction that cannot be developed based only on actions of the component parts. No holistic laws have yet been discovered, but advancing science must remain alert to such prospects.

God as the Penultimate Holistic System

As mentioned in Chapter 8, virtually all religions teach that god is a mind. Many religions also personify god, likening him to us or us to him along one or more dimensions. And I used a masculine reference to god in the prior sentence, consistent again with the majority of contemporary religious teachings and/or references.

But the seemingly undirected nature of evolution on earth, and the strong circumstantial evidence that life of different forms likely exists elsewhere, argues against linking god to the physical structure or gender of humans. In light of the modern evidence about life and the universe as reviewed to this point, it appears more logical to speak of some penultimate albeit unspecified organization, influence or intelligence (actually, or perhaps at least in some sense, a universal mind) associated with the universe, rather than a personified god with a being constrained to a design such as the human brain or body.

To summarize the model developed in this book, the brain forms the medium in which the actions of mind are expressed. Critical to understanding are the nature of both cognitive inputs and cognitive outputs from the system. For cognitive inputs, when the mind senses, perceives, interprets, and thinks, brain action physically collects and processes the data from the real world and from memory in such a fashion that, on a higher plane of abstraction, the mental processes that we call the mind play out. In turn, regarding brain outputs (volition), other mind processes represented by integrated activity in various high-level processing and output brain centers and pathways collectively produce intentional actions external to the brain. High-level processing and analysis relatively independent of input or output undoubtedly exists as well, overlapping the input and output systems in some ways. The brain is the gantry of the mind.

As developed previously, humans probably represent the youngest intelligence in the Milky Way galaxy, our home. On purely an order-of-magnitude basis, humans have been self-aware maybe 10,000 years (1,000 years is deemed too short and 100,000 years too long). As a foundation for estimates, the order-of-magnitude interval that suitable conditions have existed for intelligence to have developed elsewhere in the galaxy or the universe is unknown. But the majority of scientists who work in relevant fields seem to agree in the possibility of extraterrestrial life. These same people would probably not argue with a conservatively short time span of suitability for evolved intelligence of one billion years. In fact, organic intelligence may have existed for half the universe's existence (7.5 billion years) or more, based on the availability of proper elements of matter and of basic galactic structures. For reference, the very latest data suggests that galaxy formation peaked at about half the universe's present age, indicating that significant activity also preceded that time (a peak implies both prior and subsequent activity). Thus, we conservatively estimate that truly human-like consciousness has only existed on earth for, at most, 1/100,000 (10,000/1,000,000,000) of the time interval since human-level consciousness might have first arisen in the universe. We may be freshly born infants in the intelligence club of the cosmos.

Discussion in Chapter 8 also developed the concept of a natural (law abiding) as opposed to a supernatural (divine intervention) god. A natural god would be part of nature, and perhaps might in fact constitute nature, being manifested in the structure we see and the natural laws that we have begun to uncover. Since god is typically viewed as a mind, in essence, god in the subject scenario would be a universal (cosmic) mind integrally built into the structure of the universe. Whereas the human brain is the gantry of the human mind, the entire universe would be the gantry of a cosmic mind. In such a scenario, the cosmic mind, presumably the pinnacle of consciousness and intelligence, would represent the human concept of god.

In the spirit of the present discussion, god would represent the penultimate holistic system. Such a god might exist many, many levels of description above that of current human consciousness.

Innumerable other civilizations in the universe, with origins far back in time, may have evolved to planes of intelligence substantially beyond humans. Although pure speculation, one advanced level of consciousness, perhaps the next above the current human variety, might involve some form of collective, civilization-wide mind, overlaid later by even broader (higher-level planes of organization) mind structures yet (local, regional or fully galactic in influence, and beyond). Or, of course, completely different systems that we cannot even imagine may be in the offing. But I would certainly be personally surprised if higher-level self-organized complexity, that which exists or potentially exists above the tier presently occupied by humans, does not involve intelligence (consciousness) as a prime if not the singular defining measure of advancement. Furthermore, should we happen to find ourselves within an intelligence-centric, naturally-controlled universe, by definition, god would form the most supreme holistic organizing principle and action.

The Central Nature of Consciousness

So mind may be the answer, but what is the question? Well, the key question of all time is existence, that is, what are we and the universe doing here? Certainly, we don't know yet. And maybe we can never know. But the spirit of science has brought us tremendous new understanding in a strikingly short period of time, and it would seem quite foolish to abandon such a phenomenally successful effort.

The general approach of the scientific method to date has been one emphasizing reductionism. This system of thought and investigation attempts to decompose complex systems into smaller, tangible pieces that are simple enough for rigorous study. As a prime illustration, the stunning successes of science have reduced all known interactions in nature to the operation of four fundamental forces. In fact, work of the last three decades has begun to show how certain of the four fundamental forces are really distinct manifestations of only three or even two super forces. The goal is the ultimate in reductionism, reducing all description to a singular supreme force, the Theory Of Everything, a target of furious contemporary pursuit.

This is fundamental science at its best. And the truly stimulating and incredibly profound implications of such an accomplishment would be a fabulous triumph for humankind. But the Theory Of Everything will not really achieve its namesake unless the resulting description also encompasses the holistic nature of nature. The popularized Theory Of Everything targets the uniting of all physical forces as selective manifestations of one universal force. However, the development of a theory that unites all forces, should it come to pass, may or may not permit derivation of any underlying holistic laws. For one, we do not understand whether or not higher holistic laws await discovery. And if such holistic laws exist, we do not know if such natural legislation can be deduced from other laws or, alternatively, will require independent discovery.

We are babes in the hierarchy of intelligence. We know for a fact that the universe has become embryonically self-aware at least one time, because we are the proof. Consciousness, as the supreme operational manifestation of the mind, would seem to represent, in a word, the essence of higher-levels of the dimension of intelligence that we are addressing. And as the march of complexity continues, self-organization may push consciousness through to new, higher planes of abstraction. In fact, as stated above, my sense is that consciousness will prove to be the best descriptor as a link to higher levels of organization. Every rung on the ladder of universal complexity may bring our minds more and more into the fold of a cosmic consciousness, of which we would become a growing part.

Intelligence and consciousness are hard to define and difficult to separate. Here I refer more to consciousness, but with the realization that higher consciousness and higher intelligence seem to go hand in hand.

From the results on earth, it would appear that advances in consciousness have been richly rewarded at many tiers of animal development. And the recent breakthrough in consciousness to the tier of self-awareness has finally produced beings that can contemplate the universe and their role therein. This staggering beachhead likely carries profound significance. Out of all the incredible hierarchical advancements in the universe to which our very existence bears testimony, including such milestones as the big bang, the first formation of atoms, the origins of galaxies, the birth of stars, the creation of the heavier atomic elements, life, and even the development of intelligence, the ultimate achievement to date, the advent of self-awareness, seems to me to represent far and away the leap of abstraction with the most profound impact. Without intelligent observers, what is the point of it all?

For the latter reason, I would argue that intelligence and consciousness are prime markers of hierarchical advancement in the universe. Consciousness seems to be at least a plausible candidate for the best central measure of progress up the future stairway of complexity. But where does the staircase lead? That is the topic of the next and final chapter.

Chapter 10
The Purpose of the Universe

The Universe Is Unfinished

The goal of this book is to look at the makeup of both mind and cosmos, and to show how these two seemingly disparate entities may be inseparably related at the deepest levels. We also want to look at what present knowledge might reveal about the purpose of the universe and our role therein. The material below continues the discussion of Chapter 9 to complete the development of these thoughts. Near the end, each of the six Central Questions relating to existence and the nature and purpose of the universe are to be directly addressed.

We are witness to cosmic history in the making. We stand at a way station on a long and undefined journey. The universe has been in existence for 15 billion years, and appears destined for a future that is far more extended than its past.

But the human tendency is for the present to be pictured as the end point. We usually don't think about the fact that today's living organisms are merely the ancestors of what is to come. Our vista of human existence is even more aloof. The typical view in the Western world is based on a personal relationship with a personified god who, some say, created us in 'his' own image. In the limit, the latter construct implicitly pictures the human species as a stand-alone, fabricated entity, without ancestral forms in the past or the prospect of further evolved forms in the future. Our view of the universe is quite detached and complacent as well. Rarely is the universe pictured as a dynamic system that is different today from the past and that will continue to change as the future unfolds.

The Matter of Matter

The universe is believed to have originated in an immense explosion 15 billion years ago. This event has been dubbed, in a colossal understatement, the big bang. Interesting ideas exist about what may have caused the big bang. Regardless, we know the primordial universe was extremely hot, incredibly dense, and composed of a huge set of a few key subatomic particles and forms of radiation in a state of thermodynamic equilibrium.

The universe was rapidly cooling as it expanded in the near-term aftermath of the explosive big bang. A simple analogy would be a starburst firework bursting in the evening sky during a 4th of July display. This cooling resulted in a progressive decline in energy available for interactions between constituents. The result was that the predominant types of interactions passed through a series of stages defined by lower and lower energy ranges. At the earliest times and therefore the highest interaction energies, the classes of subatomic particles represented by, for example, protons and neutrons (constituents of the nuclei of ordinary matter today) could not endure the searing conditions. But with progressive cooling, various more familiar constituents 'froze out' as the declining temperature fell below successive interaction energy limits.

In this way, atomic nuclei and then atoms eventually coalesced, seeding space with the raw materials that would lead eventually to the partial (the process appears incomplete and open-ended) organization that we see today. But when the first atoms arose, the two simplest atoms, hydrogen and helium, made up virtually all such entities. Later, stars or small star systems, and then, much later still, full galaxies arose (this scenario follows a leading-edge hypothesis on this controversial subject based on highly-acclaimed data from the deepest space penetration yet (via the Hubble space telescope). In particular, as the matter in the universe progressively cooled, small proto-galactic fragments first formed from pre-galactic gases, dust, and smaller star systems, and then galaxies and galactic systems formed later from the successive coalescence of numerous proto-galactic fragments.

Whatever the mechanism, as the first generation of stars were born and died within any given small star system or proto-galaxy, various heavy elements (e.g., carbon; oxygen; silicon; iron) were gradually synthesized in the nuclear furnaces of certain star types. Many dying first-generation stars evolved through stages that ejected material back into the interstellar medium, substance which took the forms of subatomic particles, gas and coalesced dust grains. Then, successive new generations of stars were born from such an interstellar medium that became progressively enriched in the heavier elements as time and star generations passed. After a number of such cycles, stars and planets with a heavy-element makeup more like our solar system became possible. And, within one unremarkable spiral galaxy, the Milky Way, we sit in awe trying to comprehend the wonder of it all.

In the early moments of the big bang, all interactions are believed to have involved matter and radiation combining and annihilating in a furious unorganized fashion. But at one point, after substantial cooling, matter and radiation decoupled as interaction energies fell below a particular key threshold. Decoupling occurred, on an order-of-magnitude basis, about 100,000 years after the big bang event. During the new 'Matter Era' that followed decoupling, which continues today, matter and radiation essentially went their separate ways. In terms of tangible structure, decoupling marked the point where matter became dominant over radiation and therefore master of the whole universe. With time, the accompanying growth of self-organized complexity has been embodied by increasingly complicated assemblies of certain segments of matter, in the form of subatomic particle groupings to form atoms, atom groupings to form molecules, and in collections of molecules, atoms and mixtures thereof to create more complex substances.

Having a universe dominated by matter is very important. It is matter that self-organizes. Radiation shows no ordinary propensity to self-organize whatsoever.

Patterns of Activity

As matter grew in complexity, an amazing thing seems to have happened. In certain cases, the form of the ultimate self-organized assemblies became less and less dependent upon permanent retention of the exact same individual constituents (atoms or molecules). To use a modern example related to life, the molecules that make up our human bodies are known to be transient. Some molecules turn over faster than others, but virtually all molecules in the human body are believed to be constantly recycled and renewed. Even in the brain, the turnover of a number of component molecular classes is rather brisk, being defined in days and weeks. This startling finding means that, after a sufficient interval, our entire material being, including the brain, is totally replaced. During a lifetime, one's substantive makeup becomes reconstituted many times over.

So life is not dependent on a perpetual set of discrete molecules or atoms at all. Life must be viewed as a pattern of activity, accomplished by constituent elements whose association is transitory and constantly changing. The same is true, of course, of the brain and therefore of mind and consciousness. Our real essence, our mind, is based on a gantry that is in constant flux and that totally lacks long-term component persistence.

In other words, we come to see that life, mind and consciousness are apparently best described as a pattern of activity in self-organized arrays of ordinary matter. The pattern persists, more or less, throughout life, but the molecular constituents are constantly turning over.

This fact has enormous importance. The self-organized complexity of the most complicated system in the known universe, the human brain, is believed to have resulted from a countless series of novel, spontaneous, functionally beneficial additions to and rearrangements of collections of ordinary matter. The properties of matter and the natural laws of molecular interaction have not changed during at least most of the history of the universe. We know this to a high degree of certainty by looking far out into space (and therefore far back in time, due to the speed of light) and seeing broad evidence of a consistent physics. This also means that, during all of time, no unmanageable barriers arose that prevented matter from naturally evolving to the hallmark state where self-organized component systems became alive and self-aware. Otherwise, we would not be here.

Our existence is phenomenal. It requires very special natural laws and universe constituents to allow such an eventuality. But in addition, the finding that no insurmountable obstacles to organic life have been encountered in the universe to date gives some measure of comfort that there also may be none ahead. The universe has been here a very long time, and yet apparent advancement seems to have been continuous. While some unimagined barrier might be encountered at any time, the prospects of such an occurrence seem remote. The universe now exists at a very low average temperature, compared to the big bang, and major changes of state (phase transitions) or physics are not considered even a remote possibility.

Purposefulness: A Majestic Key

Nature certainly appears to be intelligent. Of course, as discussed elsewhere, absolutely no evidence has been found to indicate a pre-designed plan is being played out. To the contrary, the evolving universe has all the earmarks of a truly creative process, an unending, electrifying spectacle that is continuously inventing sensational new wonders seemingly without much spatial or temporal bound.

The reason that nature seems so brilliant is that most high-level self-organized systems are 'purposeful' (functionally useful). A look at life provides a striking illustration. As mentioned, life's complexity does not appear to be pre-ordained in any way. But one ingredient that makes the randomized exploratory process of organized complexity work is its insatiable bent for discovering and maintaining, based on functionality, new and improved enduring forms. Of course, the vast majority of exploratory experiments fail — the probability of any random change achieving an improvement in the ability of a complicated system to persist, function, and in the case of life, replicate, is very small. But the probability is not zero.

And nature has been shown to exploit the minuscule but finite probability of evolutionary improvement to superb advantage. The fact that a new improvement in a particular aspect of a system is successful means that some purpose is better served than before. Considered over the short term, even many new properties or capabilities that seem worthwhile at first, may ultimately lack endurance due to inflexibility, particular vulnerabilities or other weaknesses. But over the long term, evolution begets purposefulness automatically, virtually by definition. Evolution is tantamount to purposeful change. This is not by intention, but happens through the natural selection of designs that, along relevant dimensions, really perform better.

All creative work features an intimate relationship between the act of expression and the medium that the artist or designer has available. When the universe was born in the big bang, three factors are seen as setting the stage for all of history: 1) a primordial collection of radiation and a very simplistic array of matter forms; 2) the natural laws; and 3) certain initial conditions. Together, the latter three elements are considered to fully define the beginning state of the universe. The universe has spent billions of years unfolding in the wake of the big bang. The random exploratory building of self-organized complexity, acting within the constraints outlined above, coupled with unending happenstance (the details of unfolding are not predetermined) and the ruthless discriminating power of natural selection (survival of the fittest), is considered responsible for the precise cosmic landscape of today. Nature only has available the tools and substance of nature, and we exist in a self-contained, self-evolving system.

The evolution of the universe, both past and present, is envisioned as moving forth by trial and error, testing, reformulating and/or rejecting materials at hand, to mindlessly build mounting complexity. The vast majority of experiments are unsuccessful and are eliminated by natural selection. In turn, better adapted systems progressively take the place of the less capable or competitive. This endless process acts on both inanimate and living substance. The amorphous, disorganized embryonic universe found shortly after the big bang has apparently unfolded an astounding ensemble of tangible organized constituents to date. But the process is incomplete; only partial organization has been achieved; change marches on; there is nothing different about the present moment. This means, inevitably, that all sorts of imperfections pervade the world — testimony to ongoing exploration and development. It is therefore understandable that failure and inefficiency are still prevalent everywhere in the cosmos that we inhabit. Such disruptive influences are a concomitant part of matter's incessant exploration that lies at the very foundation of progress.

Many purposeful milestones have marked the developing universe up to the present. Of course, the list could be very long, limited only by the resolution chosen to label significant events. But some of the most prominent watershed occurrences would have to include the origin of entities such as atoms, molecules, stars (to produce and distribute most of the elements of the atomic table), galaxies (dynamic collections of material that, in part, form an organized environment for stars), systems of planets around stars, and the (suspected widespread) evolution of life. And it is tempting to say that the evolution of self-consciousness is yet another benchmark event. It certainly seems to be, so far at least, from the vantage point of earth. Absolutely none of the spectacular developments throughout the age of the universe would have much meaning on earth, and it would seem that the earth would have little significance in the universe at large, without human consciousness to behold the splendor and to herald the power of self-organized complexity.

Bottom-Up versus Top-Down Analysis of Existence

Most scientific discussions of existence and universal purpose begin by assembling background material to create a base for thoughts about the specific topics of interest. The same can be said regarding the present work. For example, in Chapters 5 through 7, the concept of the mind emergent from brain activity at one subordinate level and from multiple mindlets at a higher, intermediate level was developed in great detail. As another illustration, in Chapter 8, the uniformity of the underlying laws of nature and the lack of verified evidence for divine intervention was pursued, to review the case for at least our consideration of a natural as opposed to a supernatural god. In the discussion to follow, such constructs will be termed a bottom-up approach, to depict the building of global ideas from subordinate percepts.

It is also instructive to think about existence and universal purpose from a top-down standpoint. We don't have at hand as yet the supreme upper-level description of the world, and so the discussion immediately below must be clearly labeled as speculation. Nevertheless, by provisionally assuming, for the sake of analysis, that several key bits of circumstantial evidence relative to existence are true, we can explore some of the consequences. It is always valuable to examine issues from as many perspectives as possible. Ideas that may seem empty or wrong on the surface may prove to possess much more merit upon deeper scrutiny. In addition, even lines of reasoning that prove to be incorrect may trigger new ideas that finally lead to deeper understanding.

The material below develops in some detail one particular top-down picture of the universe. The chosen model has been selectively built from several of the main parameters or central topics discussed in the present book. For simplicity, to begin, each item below defines a chosen parameter (a chosen constraint) on the structure of the universe, and then, in parentheses, the converse of the chosen parameter is also mentioned to enhance clarity. The purpose is to demonstrate how various parameters can be assembled to create simple models of the universe, a crucial requirement being that the various parameters be combined so as to preserve internal consistency:

- A natural god, where nature really represents and perhaps even embodies god (versus a supernatural god, possibly existing outside of the universe [whatever that means], and with accompanying overrides of natural law);
- Predictable physical laws (versus variable laws that are ultimately indeterminate and therefore unpredictable);
- A unique universe subject to description by a Theory Of Everything (versus a world not based on one supreme logical principle and/or a singularly unified physics);
- Consciousness is the ultimate link between matter and god (consciousness plays no role, or at least no important function, in the universe);

- The universe is fundamentally holistic (versus a world where links between constituents are non-existent or unimportant); and
- The purpose of the world is universal intelligence and ultimate knowledge (versus a universe without purpose or having a purpose not centered in some way on intelligence).

It must be emphasized that the present example is very elementary. Not only are only six parameters employed, but, for each parameter, only one extreme has been contrasted against an opposite, a dichotomous approach that ignores all intermediate arrangements and more intricate detail. For perspective, by selecting one from each of the six parameter sets listed above, 64 arrangements of six items (64 universe models) are possible. Of course, many of the 64 choices are seemingly illogical, for example universes featuring a Theory Of Everything but unpredictable laws. However, many others cannot be so summarily dismissed. For illustration, the example to be discussed below employs an embellishment of one mix of parameters consistent with the main arguments of or viewpoints suggested for consideration by the present book.

Our example universe came into existence, at least as we know it, about 15 billion years ago in a stupendous primordial explosive fireball termed the big bang. The big bang initiated a fulminating expansion of the universe that continues at a declining rate today. Constant and immutable physical laws have since dictated the course of all interactions at all times. In fact, our chosen model universe is uniquely founded on one supreme logical principle, the only viable principle possible, and so all alternative universes are logically excluded.

The chosen universe embodies intelligence. The supreme logical principle is simple in its most fundamental description, is inherently self-organizing, and is majestically prolific of dazzling and yet unpredictable beauty and detail as intricate relationships spontaneously unfold. The envisioned universe is also dramatically holistic, and, after significant unfolding, is composed of an immense array of hierarchical levels of description and function. And, operationally, the ultimate hierarchical expression is a universal intelligence, a self-organizing system that has encoded in its structure all ultimate knowledge or at least the potential for all such knowledge to be eventually derived, a universal mind. It is the universal mind, the potential (if evolved consciousness must decipher the code) or actual (if the universal consciousness exists independently of evolved consciousness) universal consciousness inherent in the structure and action of all contents of the universe, that most closely corresponds to what Western human cultures have come to term god.

The profound capacity for self-organized complexity in the universe, after many billions of years, begins to progressively generate islands of primitive intelligence. One critical tier in the climb, one significant (albeit intermediate) threshold, is the self-consciousness that earth bound humanity has just achieved.

But numerous higher levels of consciousness exist, and many islands of consciousness that were born in earlier times and other cosmic places have evolved to levels substantially beyond that of humans.

At the consciousness tier where we have become self-aware, or perhaps only beginning at some higher plane that humans have not yet achieved, the beings, either individually or in some collective fashion, begin to directly interact, participate and/or contribute to the growing universal intelligence. Certainly by that time, many individual islands of intelligence will have grown greatly in zone of influence and will have perhaps joined with other island societies to create progressively larger and larger groups. And this process would continue on and on. What might be the supreme endpoint of the unfolding process, billions upon billions of years from now? It would seem that the elegance and serenity of total understanding of the self-evolving universe itself and its own consciousness (total knowledge) would be a plausible outcome.

This purely speculative scenario is presented to show how a superficial description of the world can be derived by combining various assigned parameters of model universes in assorted ways. The reader could, of course, devise many other models distinct from the above example, simply by altering some or all of the parameters employed, and/or by expanding or contracting the number of parameters from the six employed here. The limits of present knowledge do not permit a logical convergence on one unique model. However, we certainly have amassed sufficient information to provide an important framework to begin contemplating existence in an organized fashion. Such a construct would allow the average person, not just scientists, to start identifying key information and to better objectively evaluate their personal views regarding existence relative to known fact, circumstantial evidence, and cautious speculation.

For each individual, the exercise of conducting thought experiments and in exploring alternative universe models regarding existence is especially important, even though we are still faced with so many unknowns. For those who really have an interest in thinking about ultimate reality, it is imperative that opinion and belief be based on a sound, broad perspective. Due to the ever accelerating explosion of knowledge, we have passed the zone of cozy comfort where blind-faith is acceptable. Those who care, those who really seek the truth, must face the fact that the era of myths is over. We must confront the supreme question of all time — that of existence — head-on.

As described above, we have too little data to establish a particular model as the correct world view. But, based on our incomplete evidence at present, intelligence and consciousness would seem to be destined as central features in the future unfolding of the unfinished universe.

The Purpose of the Universe

The universe is governed by the laws of nature, exact and elegant in theory and application. But there is more. The formal mathematical expressions of the natural laws result in the appearance of many quantities that are collectively called the 'fundamental constants' of nature.

There is deep mystery and intrigue associated with the fundamental constants. Why do the constants have the values that they do? We know the values of the fundamental constants quite well, in many cases to exquisite precision, because we have measured and remeasured them very carefully. The hope is that the Theory of Everything, assuming that such a construct is actually achieved, will provide a derivation of at least some of the fundamental constants from first principles.

But the puzzle of the fundamental constants goes even deeper. It has been found through theoretical modeling that the values of some key constants and/ or the relative values between two or more constants must be as they are, to incredible precision, for a universe at all like ours to exist. As just one particularly glaring example among many possible illustrations (for many more, see Davies, *The Accidental Universe*, in Suggested Readings), the ratio of the electromagnetic force to the gravitational force in matter is 10^{40} (one followed by forty zeros!).

With the electromagnetic force held at its existing value, a change in the gravitational constant by a virtually inconceivable one part in 10^{40} ($1:10^{40}$) would be sufficient to rule out all normal stars like the sun (bracketed by blue giants at the large end and by red dwarfs at the small extreme) from existence at any time in the tenure of the universe. Realize that an association only agreeing to within one part in a million is $1:10^6$ and one part in a trillion (one million million) is $1:10^{12}$. Further, organic life cannot exist without normal stars, because only there are found suitable temperatures where both organic molecules and liquid water can survive for extended periods. Truly, the electromagnetic and gravitational constants must be coordinated to a staggering degree for normal stars to form at all and for us to be here to care.

Let's extend the latter background discussion to address one of our key queries: does the universe have a purpose? In my mind, several compelling bits of circumstantial evidence suggest a provisional yes. For one, we have the issue outlined above — that numerous and seemingly quite independent physical constants discovered as part of the natural laws require a phenomenal level of coordination and balance to make the present universe even possible. So far, nature's constants seem arbitrary to us, and yet, astounding precision of relative values seems to be an absolute requirement for the universe, with us in it, to exist. Also, the natural laws themselves are beautifully integrated, and their proven deep interrelationships in fact have resulted in the current hope and quest for the Theory Of Everything. In addition, the elusive and mysterious holism of the universe that has just recently come to light, coupled with the other issues identified above, provides a commanding sense of integration and unity. Finally, the very existence of life, and especially of consciousness and self-awareness, provides an extraordinary and stirring indication of some deep meaning to the universe and to existence.

It is difficult to argue that the universe is pointless, given its incredible, self-organizing form. And it is also difficult to conceive of humanity not being involved somehow. Consciousness seems to be a central issue in the cosmos, analyzed from both above and below. Looking from below, that is, from levels of simpler organization, consciousness stands as a stunning triumph of self-organized complexity that has finally resulted in evolved entities of the universe becoming self-aware. Looking down at consciousness from above, from higher levels of organization and structure, a major theme of the present argument is that consciousness may well prove to be the glue linking universal structure, function and purpose. There really doesn't seem to be much point to either underlying life or to the overlying universe (including god) without consciousness.

The consciousness conjecture, the suggestion of a really fundamental role for consciousness in the future of the universe, is a simple thought seemingly rich with potential. If, as suspected, the universe really has deep meaning, there must be threads of truth for us to find, if we only look carefully and with ingenuity. I suggest that consciousness provides one candidate phenomenon upon which substantial focus could bear dramatic insight.

Simplistically, there are two classes of universe possible, those that are contrived to some degree, and those that are not contrived at all. A contrived universe could be assembled through supernatural influences to be in working order at inception, or one that is adjusted as events unfold, or a combination of both. So we really have four possibilities for universe model classes: 1) those contrived initially; 2) one's contrived during unfolding; 3) models that are contrived both initially and during unfolding; and 4) universes that are not contrived in any way at any time (those that unfold automatically). How can we decide between these disparate models?

As this book has outlined, we have already answered the latter question. One of the most remarkable facts about the universe is that the system seems to be totally self-unfolding. For this to be true, all of the present complexity of the universe must have been inherent in the extremely simple system found during the earliest fractions of a second of the big bang. True, the number of interacting constituents at such moments were far beyond imagination. But the utter simplicity of the fundamental components at that time, compared to the dazzling diversity that even yet continues to blossom further, represents in my mind the pinnacle of ingenious beauty and elegance. Set next to any contrived universe, our self-unfolding universe, to me, is majestically exquisite and inspiring beyond comparison.

If the notion of an evolved universal mind proves to have merit, the derivation of total knowledge seems to be a plausible by-product. In other words, if the suspicion that the development of optimal functional utility (the ability to understand and best manipulate the whole cosmos) may come about through ever advancing evolution, the acquisition of total knowledge would seem to be a reasonable provisional 'purpose' to assign to the universe. Of course, our hypothetical 'purpose' must be considered within the context of the cosmos being purposeful but not following a preordained plan, an idea developed earlier. It is interesting that the concept of the universe evolving to acquire total knowledge, although derived from a different point of view, is quite consistent with the recent landmark work of Frank Tipler (*The Physics of Immortality*).

The Six Central Questions: Provisional Answers

So, at the conclusion of our journey, what can be said about the makeup of mind and the universe, their relationship, and universal purpose? We have finally arrived at a point where we can address each of the six Central Questions highlighted in the first chapter:

1. *How Does Matter Come to Create Organized Structure?* We have found that, collectively, matter is bristling with incessant capacities for emerging properties and, even more important for complex structure, self-organization. Natural happenstance creates opportunities that matter exploits to build new complexity. The substrate for emerging and self-organizing events is whatever happens to be at hand. The result is that complex systems can be seen to be made up of layer upon layer of patchwork material, each layer creating a new or extended capability or property that somehow makes the whole entity more functional. In the limit, the characteristic fingerprint of extensive emerging properties and self-organization is an inherent pattern of incessant stepwise adaptations, a cobbled substrate created through endless opportunistic improvements, leading to the particular form and function observed in the sample. The results we see now follow billions of years of countless hodgepodge fixes, resulting in an inefficient, convoluted design history that no engineer would tolerate. Relentless emerging properties and self-organization are at the very heart of all evolution, both by matter in the inanimate universe and by matter organized in a special way that we call living.

2. *What is the Nature and Makeup of Mind?* We have examined mind in general, the human brain, and its supreme earthbound form, human self-consciousness, to see how mind really relates to the matter from which it is made. We found that mind is totally dependent on and is the direct result of brain action. Mind relates to the exact same thing as brain function, but viewed on a higher plane of abstraction. The brain is truly, in every respect, the gantry of the mind. We also found that the brain is a computer, that brain function appears to be computational, and that there is no reason to suppose that computer functioning at the human level or beyond is not feasible.

3. *What is the Nature and Make-up of the Universe?* The universe is composed solely of matter and forces. Various forms of matter undergo interactions with other matter or respond to forces according to the laws of nature. At the present stage of knowledge, it seems possible that the universe is based on a very elaborate, complex but eloquent, and cryptic elaboration of perhaps one singular logical principle, or at least through laws of nature that are consistent across space and time, to create and sustain all of the complexity we behold.

4. *What is the Role of Mind in the Universe?* As we have seen, certain matter spontaneously organizes, organizes further, and then continues to organize, seemingly without end. On earth, the human mind represents the highest organized state that we have been able to observe anywhere in the cosmos to date. But life and intelligence almost certainly exist throughout the universe, and the world can be expected to go on evolving increased complexity and capability, seemingly without end. Since matter and radiation decoupled shortly after the big bang, the universe has been dominated by matter. It now appears that the cosmos is entering, or has already achieved some time in the past, an era dominated by intelligence (mind; consciousness) that is likely to extend for the rest of time (for the rest of the functional lifetime of the cosmos).

5. *What is the Meaning and Significance of Humanity?* Assuming that life is truly common in the universe, many threads of advancing intelligence can statistically be expected to sustain development long enough to actually begin to exert real effects on universe evolution. Societies of, progressively, sub-galactic, galactic and eventually super-galactic influence can be expected. Probably many, many more will fizzle out or be absorbed into more successful cultures. Even at a very early stage of advancement, such grand societies will begin to tap and later control areas of the universe itself. The reason is that enormous sources of energy will be required to optimize advancement. Ultimately, one or

more super grand societies, amalgamations of many prior successful societies, may develop to exert significant control over whole galaxies and, later, galactic systems. The ultimate in influence and control would be advancement to control aspects of the whole universe (see Frank Tipler, *The Physics of Immortality*, in the Selected Readings section at the end of the book).

Having achieved the self-conscious level of intelligence (consciousness), our human society is a real contender for a role as one of the threads of advancing intelligence. Some progressive societies may enjoy great and enduring success, sustaining themselves and advancing to lead or at least join successively advanced cultures of elevated consciousness. The ultimate endpoint of this process, if carried to the extreme, would be an all-knowing, cosmic-level social and intellectual amalgam, constituting, in essence, a universal mind. The odds for humanity are probably slim, and we have a lot of serious social problems to solve on earth before we will advance beyond anything but self-destruction. But we have our shot at glory. We are truly legitimate contenders to eventually contribute in some meaningful way, large or small, to the advancement of evolved cosmic intelligence. Regardless of our success, in my view, the future development of evolved intelligence and control on progressively larger and larger cosmic scales is virtually inevitable.

6. *What Can we Say about Universal Purpose and God?* It appears likely that increasingly powerful manifestations of consciousness (intelligence; mind) will be the hallmark of future cosmic evolution. Assuming no barriers to advancement and the passage of billions upon billions of years of evolution, a universal mind may be in the offing. Two issues logically flow from such a possibility, one related to purpose and one to the nature of god. Each is discussed in turn below.

Purpose of the Universe. One plausible result of the operation of such super-advanced intelligence over a huge span of time would be the realization of total knowledge. By total knowledge is meant, in essence, to have discovered, studied and interpreted everything about everything that is possible to know. Total knowledge seems like a legitimate candidate for the purpose (really, the crowning achievement) of the universe, with the caveat that the universe evolved naturally.

The reason for the insistence on natural universe evolution is to underscore the fact that evolving intelligence is not seen as following a pre-ordained plan and is not constrained to a pre-specified design. Intelligence may be so highly probable as to be statistically a virtual certainty. But the nature of that intelligence — its medium of embodiment (e.g., organic chemistry; some non-chemical physical mechanism [for a stunning treatment of possibilities, see Feinberg & Shapiro, 1980, in Suggested Readings) and the basic structures and interactions that constitute its fundamental processing (e.g., patterns of nerve impulses in neural nets; or again, see Feinberg & Shapiro, 1980) — are not dictated beforehand in any way.

The Nature of God. If all of the other provisional answers to the Central Questions outlined above should prove correct, there are important alternatives that we should at least consider to a god of the type generally purported by Western religions. The growing collective consciousness (intelligence) of sub-cosmic and eventually cosmic society may in fact rise to accompany or even actually become a natural god.

To expand on the latter notion of a natural god, such a global influence could be of two types. One would be a natural god that is distinct from evolved intelligence, and that somehow is responsible for nature or perhaps actually constitutes nature — a perpetual natural god. The other possibility is that evolved intelligence might progressively grow, in the absence of a perpetual natural god, to become the ultimate controlling influence of the universe — an evolved natural god. An evolved natural god would not always have existed but rather would progressively develop during the tenure of the universe.

In the case of a perpetual natural god, it would not seem obvious that evolved intelligence would be eventually assimilated into the perpetual god proper, and so the perpetual natural god and the evolved intelligence might forever remain distinct. However, for an evolving natural god, progressively emerging intelligence would constitute an evolved natural god all along, by logical identity — evolving intelligence and god would always be one and the same.

In any case, by design, we have addressed what are really the ultimate questions of all time. The objective here has been to see what current scientific knowledge can tell us about matter, existence, and purpose, and further to embellish known fact with cautious speculation.

As We Enter the End Game

In perspective, we see that the human mind appears to be the result of an incredible, hierarchically-arranged system of physiologically interacting sub-systems and sub-subsystems, fashioned totally from spontaneously organized ordinary matter. By extension, we have taken the view that life and mind can logically arise elsewhere, and almost certainly has formed at many other cosmic locations and times. Therefore, mind (consciousness) is most likely a very natural component of universe evolution that may in fact best codify the extent of cosmic advancement.

Advancement is believed to be truly the correct term here. One could try to argue that the universe is really not advancing, but is merely changing in some non-progressive or even negative way. However, it is virtually certain that the cosmos is advancing to yet higher levels of complexity, as developed in more detail below.

The universe is a dynamic system that:
a) had a definite beginning when the useful organization of its components was very low; and
b) is moving toward an end where useful activity will again be very low and eventually impossible (either a heat death or a Big Crunch; see Chapter 8). We also know that many processes have occurred since the cosmic origin to create the wealth of organization that we witness today.

Here, it is illuminating to imagine a two-dimensional, continuous graph of useful organization versus time. Our universe has two minimum values along the horizontal time axis — a beginning and an end — and values with significant positive magnitudes of useful organization in between (negative or zero levels of useful organization between the endpoints makes little sense). So there must be a maximum of useful organization in the curve somewhere between the minimal values at either end, in our past, our future, or now. Earlier in the book, the case was developed for a universe of today that has not as yet peaked and is still rife with potential for further self-organization. Apparently, the maximum of useful organization is in our future.

For a universal mind to eventually evolve, we estimated above that the window of opportunity is tens of billions of years. For the subject process to happen, individual intelligent societies would need to progressively colonize their local cosmic realms at a reasonable rate, and learn to control key energy sources within their growing spheres of influence. (Importantly, plausible estimates exist for human colonization of the Milky Way galaxy in less than a million years.) In at least some cases, such societies must also be smart enough by the time they bump into other expanding societies to join together for the mutual benefit of further, more grand expansion. Then, it would be necessary for the density of initial intelligent societies to be high enough so that growing oases of ever-mounting intelligence could progressively carry out compounded mergers on a sub-cosmic and then cosmic scales within the available tens of billions of years. Finally, the ultimate societal amalgam would have to complete the acquisition of total knowledge.

While these tasks may seem daunting to earth bound humans, it is interesting that the prospect of total knowledge does not seem to be at all impossible. In fact, Frank Tipler, in his previously cited book *The Physics of Immortality*, builds an intriguing argument that the acquisition of total knowledge by far-future intelligence is virtually inevitable and that sufficient time is in fact available.

In conclusion, let's define the 'End Game' as the Consciousness Era of the universe. During most of cosmic history through today, at least as far as we know, matter has been the dominating influence. Matter certainly has been dominant over mind here on earth. But we have seen that matter appears to beget consciousness, almost certainly, given enough time. The central feature of the End Game may very well be a contest of sorts. Among intelligent societies, ultimate winners will be those that continue to sustain themselves and grow in intellectual prowess and cosmic influence. Losers will fail to sustain their society, or become swallowed up by more successful groups without being able to influence any resulting amalgams.

The Consciousness Era may have actually begun at some earlier time elsewhere in the universe. As we have seen, it appears that the universe in general may have been able to give birth to life and ultimately to intelligence long ago, most likely countless times over, at various places in the vast reaches of the cosmic stage. But we on earth are just entering the Consciousness Era now.

Of course, there is always the possibility that the universe has no purpose and so we don't either. Maybe the universe just appeared, and the existence of inherent self-organizing potentiality was pure accident. Or our visible corner of a large or infinite universe may form but an insignificant irregularity in an otherwise unorganized "un-system." We have no way at present to rule out such possibilities, any more than we can reject a supernatural god or any other scenario. But the breathtaking beauty and cunning brilliance of natural law and the extreme improbability of the universe we behold, especially the existence of life and self-awareness, makes me believe that there lurks method in the madness, and that, somehow, the madness involves us.

Suggested Reading

A particular point of view was put forth in this book, the purpose being to maintain coherency for those readers with a less technical background. In turn, my real goal was to challenge the reader to adopt their own view. In this vein, as guidance for further reading, the selections listed below were not chosen to necessarily support or complement concepts developed in this book. Listings represent works deemed relevant to the present book, but no attempt was made to make the list complete. Due apologies are offered to authors of many fine books and other treatments that were not included.

Albert DZ, 1994. *Bohm's Alternative to Quantum Mechanics.* Scient. Am. 270:58-67

Bailey J, 1996. *After Thought: The Challenge to Human Thinking.* Basic Books

Bak P, Chen K, 1991. *Self-Organized Criticality.* Scient. Am. 264:46-53

Bak P, 1996. How Nature Works: The Science of Self-Organized Criticality. Copernicus

Barrow, JD, 1990. *The World Within the World.* Oxford Univ. Press

Barrow JD, 1994. *Pi in the Sky: Counting, Thinking, and Being.* Little, Brown

Bohm D, 1983. *Wholeness and the Implicate Order.* Ark Paperbacks

Bower B, 1992. *Consciousness Raising: Theories Abound regarding the Vexing Nature of Conscious Experience.* Sci. News 142:232-5

Briggs J, Peat FD, 1990. *Turbulent Mirror: An Illustrated Guide to Chaos Theory and the Science of Wholeness.* Harper Perennial

Brill D, 1994. *Erectus Rising.* Discover 15(9):80-9

Bunge M, 1980. *The Mind-Body Problem: A Psychobiological Approach.* Pergamon Press

Cairns-Smith AG, 1986. *Seven Clues to the Origin of Life: A Scientific Detective Story.* Cambridge Univ. Press

Calvin WH, 1996. *The Cerebral Code: Thinking a Thought in the Mosaics of the Mind.* MIT Press

Calvin WH, 1996. *How Brains Think: Evolving Intelligence, Then and Now.* Basic Books

Casti JL, 1994. *Complexification: Explaining a Paradoxical World Through the Science of Surprise.* Harper Collins

Chaisson E, 1989. *The Life Era: Cosmic Selection and Conscious Evolution.* Norton

Chalmers DJ, 1996. *The Conscious Mind: In Search of a Fundamental Theory.* Oxford Univ. Press

Chown M, 1996. *Afterglow of Creation: From the Fireball to the Discovery of Cosmic Ripples.* Univ. Sci. Bks.

Cornwell J, editor, 1995. *Nature's Imagination: The Frontiers of Scientific Vision.* Oxford Univ. Press

Coveney P, Highfield R, 1995. *Frontiers of Complexity: The Search for Order in a Chaotic World.* Fawcett

Crick F, 1982. *Life Itself: Its Origin and Nature.* Touchstone

Croswell K, 1995. *The Alchemy of the Heavens: Searching for Meaning in the Milky Way.* Anchor Books

Davies P, 1979. *The Forces of Nature.* Cambridge Univ. Press

Davies P, 1982. *The Accidental Universe.* Cambridge Univ. Press

Davies P, 1984. *God and the New Physics.* Touchstone

Davies P, 1989. *The Cosmic Blueprint: New Discoveries in Nature's Creative Ability to Order the Universe.* Touchstone

Davies P, 1993. *The Mind of God: The Scientific Basis for a Rational World.* Touchstone

Davies P, 1996. *Are We Alone? Philosophical Implications of the Discovery of Extraterrestrial Life.* Basic Books

Davies P, Gribbin J, 1992. *The Matter Myth: Dramatic Discoveries that Challenge our Understanding of Physical Reality.* Touchstone

Dawkins R, 1996. *Climbing Mount Improbable.* Norton

Delbruck M, 1986. *Mind from Matter? An Essay on Evolutionary Epistemology.* Blackwell Scientific Publications

Dennett D, 1995. *Darwin's Dangerous Idea: Evolution and the Meanings of Life.* Simon & Schuster

Dennett D, 1996. *Kinds of Minds: Toward an Understanding of Consciousness.* Basic Books

Devlin K, 1997. *Goodbye, Descartes: The End of Logic and the Search for a New Cosmology of the Mind.* Wiley

Dickey JS Jr, 1996. *On the Rocks: Earth Science for Everyone.* Wiley

Donald M, 1993. *Origins of the Modern Mind: Three Stages in the Evolution of Culture and Cognition.* Harvard Univ. Press

Dunbar R, 1997. *Grooming, Gossip, and the Evolution of Language.* Harvard Univ. Press

Dyson F, 1997. *Imagined Worlds.* Harvard Univ. Press

Fackelmann KA, 1994. *The Conscious Mind.* Sci. News 146:10-11

Feinberg G, Shapiro, R, 1980. *Life Beyond Earth: The Intelligent Earthling's Guide to Life in the Universe.* Morrow

Ferris T, 1993. *The Mind's Sky: Human Intelligence in a Cosmic Context.* Bantam Books

Ferris T, 1997. *The Whole Shebang: A State-of-the-Universe(s) Report.* S&S

Feynman RP, 1988. *QED: The Strange Theory of Light and Matter.* Princeton Univ.

Field RJ, 1985. *Chemical Organization in Time and Space.* Amer. Scientist 73:142-150

Freeman WJ, 1991. *The Physiology of Perception.* Scient. Am. 264:78-85

Gazzaniga MS, 1988. *Mind Matters: How Mind and Brain Interact to Create our Conscious Lives.* Houghton Mifflin

Gazzaniga MS, 1992. *Nature's Mind: The Biological Roots of Thinking, Emotions, Sexuality, Language, and Intelligence.* Basic Books

Gell-Mann M, 1994. *The Quark and the Jaguar: Adventures in the Simple and the Complex.* Freeman

Gilmore R, 1995. *Alice in Quantumland: An Allegory of Quantum Physics.* Copernicus

Goleman D, 1986. *Vital Lies, Simple Truths: The Psychology of Self-Deception.* Touchstone

Goodwin B, 1994. *How the Leopard Changed its Spots. The Evolution of Complexity.* Scribner & Sons

Gould JL, Gould CG, eds, 1989. *Life at the Edge.* Freeman

Greenfield SA, 1995. *Journey to the Center of the Mind: Toward a Science of Consciousness.* Freeman

Greenspan SI, 1997. *The Growth of the Mind: And the Endangered Origins of Intelligence.* Addison-Wesley

Gribbin J, 1986. *In Search of the Big Bang: Quantum Physics and Cosmology.* Bantam Books

Gribbin J, 1988. *The Omega Point: The Search for the Missing Mass and the Ultimate Fate of the Universe.* Bantam Books

Gribbin J, Rees M, 1989. *Cosmic Coincidences: Dark Matter, Mankind, and Anthropic Cosmology.* Bantam Books

Gribbin J, 1996. *Companion to the Cosmos.* Little Brown

Hawking S, 1990. *A Brief History of Time: From the Big Bang to Black Holes.* Bantam Books

Hofstadter DR, Dennett DC, 1981. *The Mind's I: Fantasies and Reflections on Self and Soul.* Bantam Books

Holland JH, 1996. *Hidden Order: How Adaptation Builds Complexity.* Addison-Wesley

Hooper J, Teresi D, 1986. *The 3-Pound Universe.* Jeremy P. Tarcher

Horgan J, 1992. *Quantum Philosophy.* Scient. Am. 267:94-104

Horgan J, 1996. *The End of Science: Facing the Limits of Knowledge in the Twilight of the Scientific Age.* Addison-Wesley

Hoyle F, 1977. *Ten Faces of the Universe.* Freeman

Hunt M, 1983. *The Universe Within: A New Science Explores the Mind.* Touchstone

Jeans J, 1981. *Physics and Philosophy.* Dover

Kaku M, Thompson J, 1995. *Beyond Einstein: The Cosmic Quest for the Theory of Everything.* Anchor

Kane G, 1995. *The Particle Garden: Our Universe as Understood by Particle Physicists.* Addison-Wesley

Kandel, RS, 1980. *Earth and Cosmos: A Book Relating the Environment of Man on Earth to the Environment of Earth in the Cosmos.* Pergamon Press

Kauffman S, 1995. *At Home in the Universe: The Search for the Laws of Self-Organization and Complexity.* Oxford Univ. Press

Larison-Cudmore LL, 1978. *The Center of Life: A Natural History of the Cell.* Quadrangle Books

Layzer D, 1991. *Cosmogenesis: The Growth of Order in the Universe.* Oxford Univ. Press

LeDoux J, 1996. *The Emotional Brain: The Mysterious Underpinnings of Emotional Life.* Simon & Schuster

Lipkin R, 1994. *From Proteins to Protolife.* Sci. News 146:58-9

Litvak S, Senzee AW, 1986. *Toward a New Brain: Evolution and the Human Mind.* Prentice-Hall

Mammana DL, McCarthy DW, 1996. *Other Suns, Other Worlds? The Search for Extrasolar Planetary Systems.* St. Martin

McCrone J, 1991. *The Ape That Spoke: Language and the Evolution of the Human Mind.* Avon Books

McLeish J, 1994. *The Story of Numbers: How Mathematics has Shaped Civilization.* Fawcett

McSween HY Jr, 1997. *Fanfare for Earth: The Origin of Our Planet and Life.* St. Martin

Minsky M, 1988. *The Society of Mind.* Touchstone

Mithen S, 1996. *The Prehistory of the Mind: The Cognitive Origins of Art, Religion, and Science.* Thames Hudson

Motz L, Weaver JH, 1995. *The Story of Mathematics.* Avon

Murchie, G, 1978. *The Seven Mysteries of Life: An Exploration in Science and Philosophy.* Houghton Mufflin

Murchie G, 1967. *Music of the Spheres. Vol I. The Macrocosm: Planets, Stars, Galaxies, Cosmology.* Dover

Murchie G, 1967. *Music of the Spheres. Vol II. The Microcosm: Matter, Atoms, Waves, Radiation, Relativity.* Dover

Newborn M, 1997. *Kasperov versus Deep Blue: Computer Chess Comes of Age.* Springer-Verlag

Ornstein R, 1992. *The Evolution of Consciousness: The Origins of the Way We Think.* Touchstone

Pagels HR, 1983. *The Cosmic Code: Quantum Physics as the Language of Nature.* Bantam Books

Pagels HR, 1986. *Perfect Symmetry: The Search for the Beginning of Time.* Bantam Books

Peak D, Frame M, 1994. *Chaos Under Control: The Art and Science of Complexity.* Freeman

Peat FD, 1987. *Synchronicity: The Bridge Between Matter and Mind.* Bantam Books

Peat FD, 1988. *Superstrings and the Search for The Theory of Everything.* Contemporary Books

Peterson I, 1990. *Beyond the Z: The Latest Generation of High-Powered Particle Accelerators Has Produced No Real Surprises. What's Next?* Sci. News 138:204-6

Peterson I, 1995. *Newton's Clock: Chaos in the Solar System.* Freeman

Penrose R, 1991. *The Emperor's New Mind: Concerning Computers, Minds, and the Laws of Physics.* Penguin Books

Priest S, 1991. *Theories of the Mind.* Houghton Mifflin

Prigogine I, Stengers I, 1984. *Order out of Chaos: Man's New Dialog with Nature.* Bantam Books

Reeves H, 1985. *Atoms of Silence: An Exploration of Cosmic Evolution.* MIT Press

Rensberger B, 1996. *Life Itself: Exploring the Realm of the Living Cell.* Oxford Univ. Press

Rensberger B, 1996. *Instant Biology: From Single Cells to Human Beings, and Beyond.* Columbine

Resnick M, 1997. *Turtles, Termites, and Traffic Jams: Explorations in Massively Parallel Microworlds.* MIT Press

Restak R, 1995. *Brainscapes: An Introduction to What Neuroscience Has Learned About the Structure, Function, and Abilities of the Brain.* Hyperion

Rigutti M, 1984. *A Hundred Billion Stars.* MIT Press

Riordan M, Schramm DN, 1991. *The Shadows of Creation: Dark Matter and the Structure of the Universe.* Freeman

Ronan CA, 1996. *Science Explained: The World of Science in Everyday Life.* Holt

Rose S, 1976. *The Conscious Brain.* Vintage Books

Rose S, 1993. *The Making of Memory: From Molecules to Mind.* Anchor Books

Rosenfield I, 1993. *The Strange, Familiar, and Forgotten: An Anatomy of Consciousness.* Vintage Books

Rucker R, 1984. *The Fourth Dimension: A Guided Tour of the Higher Universes.* Houghton Mifflin

Russell P, 1979. *The Brain Book.* Dutton

Ruthen R, 1993. *Adapting to Complexity.* Scient. Am. 268:128-140

Sagan C, Shklovskii LS, 1966. *Intelligent Life in the Universe.* Holden-Day

Sagan C, 1995. *The Demon-Haunted World: Science as a Candle in the Dark.* Random

Savage-Rumbaugh S, Lewin R, 1994. *Ape at the Brink.* Discover 15(9):91-8

Schacter DL, 1996. *Searching for Memory: The Brain, the Mind, and the Past.* Basic Books

Schramm DN, Steigman G, 1988. *Particle Accelerators Test Cosmological Theory.* Scient. Am. 258:66-72

Scott A, 1995. *Stairway to the Mind: The Controversial New Science of Consciousness.* Copernicus

Searle J, 1984. *Minds, Brains and Science.* Harvard Univ. Press

Shimony A, 1988. *The Reality of the Quantum World.* Scient. Am. 258:46-53

Silk J, 1980. *The Big Bang. The Creation and Evolution of the Universe.* Freeman

Smith CG, 1985. *Ancestral Voices: Language and the Evolution of Human Consciousness.* Prentice-Hall

Smoot G, Davidson K, 1994. *Wrinkles in Time.* Avon

Springer SP, Deutsch G, 1985. *Left Brain, Right Brain.* Freeman

Talbot M, 1992. *The Holographic Universe.* Harper Perennial

Tank DW, Hopfield JJ, 1987. *Collective Computation in Neuronlike Circuits.* Scient. Am. 257:104-114

Tattersall I, 1996. *The Fossil Trail: How We Know What We Think We Know About Human Evolution.* Oxford Univ. Press

Thomsen DE, 1985. *The Quantum Universe: From Creation Ex Nihilo to the Omega Point, We're on a Roller Coaster We Can't Stop.* Sci. News. 128: 72-4

Tipler FJ, 1995. *The Physics of Immortality: Modern Cosmology, God and the Resurrection of the Dead.* Anchor Books

Trefil J, 1997. *Are We Unique? A Scientist Explores the Unparalleled Intelligence of the Human Mind.* Wiley

Waldrop MM, 1993. *Complexity. The Emerging Science at the Edge of Order and Chaos.* Touchstone

Weinberg S, 1979. *The First Three Minutes. A Modern View of the Origin of the Universe.* Bantam Books

Weinberg S, 1993. *Dreams of a Final Theory. The Scientific Search for the Ultimate Laws of Nature.* Vintage Books

Wesson R, 1991. *Beyond Natural Selection.* MIT Press

White F, 1990. *The SETI Factor: How the Search for Extraterrestrial Intelligence is Changing Our View of the Universe and Ourselves.* Walker

Whybrow PC, 1997. *A Mood Apart: Depression, Mania, and Other Afflictions of the Self.* Basic Books

Wolf FA, 1981. *Taking the Quantum Leap: The New Physics for Non-Scientists.* Harper & Row

Wolf FA, 1995. *The Dreaming Universe: A Mind-Expanding Journey into the Realm where Psyche and Physics Meet.* Touchstone

Young, LB, 1993. *The Unfinished Universe.* Oxford Univ. Press

Zohar D, 1990. *The Quantum Self: Human Nature and Consciousness Defined by the New Physics.* Quill

Index

M

About the Author

While growing up in the infectious beauty of the Pacific Northwest and the emerging bustle of Portland, Oregon, author Wayne Fields developed an early interest in the universe and existence. Even in grade school, he came to see the world as making sense and recognized a compelling need for deeper understanding. This was a major force in his emphasis on the physical sciences in college, where he received his BS in Science from Oregon State University (1963). During college, Wayne discovered a strong attraction to the life sciences, and in particular how the physical sciences can be employed to explain the much higher complexity of the biological world. Academic pursuit of these inspiring ideas led Wayne Fields to a Ph.D. in Physiology from Oregon Health Sciences University (1969) with a primary focus in neurophysiology.

Dr. Fields interest in teaching, research, and product development led him to employment with NASA, the Oregon Health Sciences University, and the medical device industry. He was the co-owner and director of a private product and business development firm. Now in his mid-50s, Dr. Fields has retired from formal work to pursue his passion of researching and writing about existence, mind, and cosmos, life-long subjects he feels to be tightly bound at the highest levels of analysis.

ABOUT THE PUBLISHER

Our imprints include books in a variety of fields and disciplines which emphasize our relationship to the rising planetary consciousness. Literature which relates to the ascension process, personal growth, and our relationship to extraterrestrials is our primary focus. We are also developing a line of beautifully illustrated children's books, which deal with all aspects of spirituality. The list that follows is only a sample of our current offerings. To obtain a complete catalog, contact us at the address shown at the back of this book.

Ascension Books

An Ascension Handbook, by Tony Stubbs. A practical "how to" manual which describes the ascension process in detail, how we create reality, and who we really are. The book also includes an "Ascension Toolkit"—exercises and practices to help you integrate Spirit into your daily life. — *ISBN 1-880666-08-1, $12.95*

Bridge Into Light: Your Connection to Spiritual Guidance, by Pam and Fred Cameron. Lovingly offers many step-by-step exercises on how to meditate and how to channel, and gives ways to invoke the protection and assistance of the Masters. (Companion tape available.) — *ISBN 1-880666-07-3, $11.95*

What Is Lightbody? Archangel Ariel, channeled by Tashira Tachi-ren. Articulates a twelve-level model for the ascension process, leading to the attainment of our Light Body. Recommended in *An Ascension Handbook*, this book gives many invocations and procedures to assist us on our journey home. (Related tapes available.) — *ISBN 1-880666-25-1, $12.95*

Heart Initiation, by Julianne Everett. Answers many questions about the process of awakening, such as: Does self-mastery have to be so difficult? Why is love so important? How do we become truly free? What are the challenges and rewards of conscious ascension? This book assists you in surrendering to your own spirit with grace, fun, and ease. — *ISBN 1-880666-36-7 $14.95*

My Ascension Journal by Nicole Christine. Transform yourself and your life by using the journalizing methods given in this book. Includes several real-life examples from the author's own journals, plus blank pages on which to write your own ascension story. This quality bound edition will become a treasured keepsake to be re-read over and over again. — *ISBN 1-880666-18-9, $11.95*

Living Mastery: The Expression of Your Divinity by Joanna Cherry, is an adventure into our unlimited possibilities. We are pioneers exploring a frontier unimaginable before, where each of us will realize how great we truly are. Through our oneness with the divine, the infinite One, we are returning to our ancient, forgotten, natural mastery. We recognize *everything* as divine, including our physical body, and Earth herself as paradise. It is why we are here. You are invited to walk your own unique path with greater certainty and joy, from believing you were limited to knowing you are divine. A deep look at life— including self-empowerment, purpose, abundance, service, immortality, ascension, and more—will speed you along your way. — *ISBN 1-880666-68-5, $12.95*

Kirael: The Great Shift by Fred Sterling. Kirael is one of the entities who are guiding humanity through the upcoming changes, and brings us much valuable advice about what to expect, how to prepare, and how to handle the changes with grace and ease. Contains new insights on such topics as the Great Shift, relationships, the Galactic Brotherhood, the lost legends of Lemuria and Atlantis, Ascension, and much, much more.— *ISBN 1-880666-76-6 $14.95*

Tales and Teachings

Gifts: Remembering the Now, by Yolanda Zigarmi Martin. The author undergoes spontaneous past life regressions and interacts with her other incarnations. Spanning thousands of years, Yolanda's insights reveal the very essence of our existence, the nature of death, and our relationship with our Creator. — *ISBN 1-880666-59-6 $13.95*

Lady From Atlantis, by Robert V. Gerard. Shar Dae, the future empress of Atlantis, is suddenly transported onto a rain-soaked beach in modern America. There she meets her twin flame and discovers her mission: to warn the people of planet Earth to mend their ways before Mother Earth takes matters in her own hands! — *ISBN 1-880666-21-9, $12.95*

Intuition by Design, by Victor R. Beasley, Ph.D. A boxed set of 36 IQ (Intuition Quotient) Cards contain consciousness-changing geometry on one side and transformational verse on the other. The companion book tells you the many ways to use the cards in all aspects of your life. An incredible gift to yourself and someone you love. Bring your life into alignment with the Higher Mind of Source. — *ISBN 1-880666-22-7, $21.95*

The Extraterrestrial Vision by Gina Lake. Through Gina, Theodore, a nonphysical entity, tells us what we need to know about our extraterrestrial heritage and how to prepare for direct contact with those civilizations which will soon be appearing in our midst. Provides a valuable "who's who" of ETs. — *ISBN 1-880666-19-7, $13.95*

ET Contact: Blueprint for a New World, by Gina Lake. Through Gina, the Confederation of Planets tells us what life on Earth will be like following mass contact with extraterrestrials, how institutions such as education, politics, government, business, the arts and the media, and what we must do to prepare at both personal and planetary levels. — *ISBN 1-880666-62-6, $12.95*

Navigating the 90s by Deborah Soucek. Practical ways to deal with today's chaotic times, and claim your sovereignty when others would trample it. Packed with pertinent observations and useful exercises on topics like loving yourself and how the words you use so casually are really trapping you.
— *ISBN 1-880666-47-2, $13.95*

Angels of the Rays by Johanna. A set of twelve beautifully produced, full-color Angel pictures with supporting descriptions, messages, rays, and invocations. Includes a push-out color card for each Angel. Makes a stunning gift!
— *ISBN 1-880666-34-0, $19.95. (Additional card sets $12.95)*

Voice in the Mirror: Will The Final Apocalypse Be Averted? by Lee Shargel. In this first novel of *The Chulosian Chronicles*, Lee skilfully weaves fact and fiction to tell a thrilling story of extraterrestrials using the Hubble telescope to warn of impending planetary disaster. But that's only the beginning of the story. How will the ETs presence influence life on Earth.
— *ISBN 1-880666-54-5, $23.95.*

The Corporate Mule: Don't Give Up Your Soul for the Company Goal, by Robert V. Gerard. In this "slice of life," follow a young man's maturation as his idealism is shattered by the truth of corporate reality and he opens to his soul's purpose for his current lifetime. Look for aspects of yourself in the main character and learn from his mistakes. —*ISBN 1-880666-04-9, $14.95*

Solarian Legacy: Metascience and a New Renaissance by Paul Von Ward. Questioning why most people ignore their own experience in favor of conventional scientific and religious dogma, Paul distills knowledge from ancient wisdom to modern physics, to present a compelling and audacious synthesis that rips away blinders and empowers the reader. Metascience reveals humanity's true legacy: a rich, forgotten prehistory; assistance from other conscious beings; and untapped inner senses and powers. The text challenges cherished views of reality, revealing a startling, but satisfying appreciation of greater human potential in co-creation of the universe itself. It refreshingly describes the "legacy's" implications for everything from healthcare to political institutions, including effective human relations. — *ISBN 1-880666-75-8, $15.00*

The Call Goes Out: Messages from the Earth's Cetaceans, by Dianne Robbins. A series of messages received telepathically from the cetacean species—whales and dolphins—who make a simple, direct plea from the heart to stop killing those who are trying to help us. The book graphically spells out why they are here on Earth, how they work with extra-terrestrials, and how we interfere with their mission. They make an impassioned plea for us to stop whaling and cease using fishing nets, and also to free whales and dolphins in captivity. Readers will have their eyes opened to the rich family and cultural life of another intelligent species on this planet. — *ISBN 1-880666-64-2, $12.95*

From Sirius To Earth: A Therapist Discovers a Soul Exchange, by Evelyn Fuqua, Ph.D. and Athor. Through hypnosis, Dr. Evelyn Fuqua leads Rose-Athor through a fascinating journey to discover that when the child, Rose, was three years old, a Soul Exchange took place in which Rose left and was replaced by Athor, an aspect of one of the Council of Twelve on the etheric plane of the star system of Sirius. This is a "must read" book for anyone wanting to understand the connection between humanity and extraterrestrials in a spiritual context. This inspirational true story of one woman's journey to understand herself from a soul level will assist you in your own soul's evolution.
— *ISBN 1-880666-65-0, $14.95*

Jewels within a Teardrop by Toni Salerno. Poetry is the artwork of the literary world, and Jewels within a Teardrop offers both: 16 beautiful, evocative paintings by the author, and a fine anthology of haunting poems that explore the nature of the universe, the Creator, humanity, and our relationships with each other. Unhampered by the linearity of prose, Toni uses the poet's freedom to paint images that resonate with our deepest hopes and fears, and joys and pain—hopes for a new age and the fear that blocks us from it, the pain of separation from our Creator or a lover, and the joy of reunion. Toni's poetry is a true roller-coaster for the emotions.— *ISBN 1-880666-74-X $14.95*

Eastern Sunrise, Western Sunset: The Cycle of Civilizations by Dr. Takuro Kishine. In a broad sweep, spanning six millennia of recorded history, Dr. Kishine explores the 800-year alternating cycles of the ascent and descent of Eastern and Western civilizations. Dr. Kishine's research points to the inevitable decline of the West's pre-eminence in the next century, with the corresponding ascent of Eastern cultures. From DNA to Darwinism, and deforestation to Descartes, Dr. Kishine leaves no stone unturned in his penetrating analysis of what is to come. The cosmos itself requires alternation between the left-brained materialism of the West and the right-brained spirituality of the East. The West must once again step down as a new era of Eastern influence dawns on our planet. — *ISBN 1-880666-57-X, $23.95 (hardcover)*

Love and Hope: A Message for the New Millenium, by Kiyo Sasaki Monro. A delightfully written book of wisdom that the author has gleaned on her path, with autobiographical notes, and an extensive question-and-answer section derived from live presentations. An ideal "starter book" for someone new to metaphysics such as a gift for a friend. — *ISBN 1-880666-56-1, $14.95*

Don't Send Me Any Rainbows, a true story by Patricia Fenton. This autobiographical novel is a comical romp through the Last Great Adventure of the author's beloved Aunt Allie who is dying of cancer. The author eases Aunt Allie's passage into the Great Beyond with Mystery School teachings, nutritional advice, her own personal visions, and good, old-fashioned common sense in her approach to life and death. *Don't Send Me Any Rainbows* is a delightful, charming story that gives new meaning to "death with dignity." Sparkling dialogue, characters that touch your heart *and* your funny bone—it is a must read for anyone with a loved one with a terminal illness. — *ISBN 1-880666-66-9, $14.95*

Handling Verbal Confrontation: Take the Fear Out of Facing Others by Robert V. Gerard. Lack of effective confrontation skills is behind most of the problems at home or in the workplace. The book begins by describing the problems of poor communications and moves into accurate communications, based on a model of how we communicate. Next, the Confrontation Model lays the foundation for the entire technique, the basis of which is the 1-2-3 Approach: the Intro, the Clear Concise Statement, and the Fix. Learn also about ploys and strategies, such as the Rebuttal, the Overshoot, and the Firm Stand. Whether you are the head of a corporation, in a committed relationship, or the parents of teenagers, you can use these verbal confrontation techniques to ensure win-win-win confrontations. Otherwise, you're just arguing!
— *ISBN 1-880666-05-7, $14.95*

DNA Healing Techniques by Robert V. Gerard, Vianna, and Dr. Todd Ovokaitys. Cellular healing and rejuvenation are two of the most talked about healing topics today. Oughten House Foundation introduces you to this fascinating topic, and gives you three very powerful ascension tools that anyone can begin using with just a few hours practice. — *ISBN 1-880666-77-4, $8.95*